THE WALKER BEDTIME BOOK

OVER 100 FAVOURITE STORIES & RHYMES

WALKER BOOKS

AND SUBSIDIARIES

LONDON • BOSTON • SYDNEY

Contents

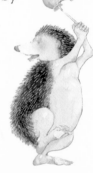

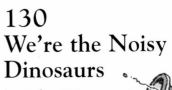

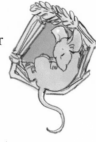

THIS IS THE BEAR

by Sarah Hayes
illustrated by Helen Craig

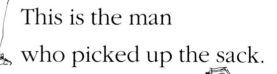

This is the man
who picked up the sack.

This is the driver
who would not come back.

This is the bear
who went to the dump
and fell on the pile
with a bit of a bump.

This is the bear
who fell in the bin.

This is the dog
who pushed him in.

This is the boy
who took the bus
and went to the dump
to make a fuss.

This is the man
in an awful grump
who searched and searched
and searched the dump.

This is the bear
all cold and cross
who did not think
he was really lost.

This is the dog
who smelled the smell
of a bone and a tin
and a bear as well.

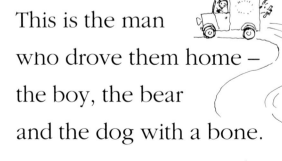

This is the man
who drove them home –
the boy, the bear
and the dog with a bone.

This is the bear
all lovely and clean
who did not say
just where he had been.

This is the boy
who knew quite well,
but promised his friend
he would not tell.

And this is the boy
who woke up in the night
and asked the bear
if he felt all right –
and was very surprised
when the bear shouted out,
"How soon can we have
another day out?"

Daisy Dare

by Anita Jeram

Daisy Dare did things her friends were far too scared to do.

"Just dare me," she said. "Anything you like. I'm never, *ever* scared!"

So they dared her to walk the garden wall.

They dared her to eat a worm.

They dared her to stick out her tongue at Miss Crumb.
And she did!

One day, Daisy's friends thought of a really scary dare to do. They whispered it to Daisy.

"I'm not doing that!" she said.

"Daisy Dare-not!" they laughed.

Daisy took a deep breath. "All right," she said. "I'll do it."

This was the dare: to take the bell off the cat's collar.

The cat was asleep. That was good. The bell slipped off easily. That was good too. But Daisy's hands trembled so much that the bell tinkled, the cat woke up and that was very, very bad!

Daisy ran and ran as fast as she could, back to her friends, through the garden gate, and into the house where the cat couldn't follow.

"Phew!" said Billy.

"Wow!" gasped Joe.

"You're the bravest, most daring mouse in the whole world!" shouted Contrary Mary.

Daisy Dare grinned with pride.

"Just dare me," she said. "Anything you like… I'm only *sometimes* scared!"

11

Chi-li the Panda

by Derek Hall • illustrated by John Butler

Chi-li loves to play with his mother. Sometimes she gives him a piggy-back and then he feels as tall as a grown-up panda.

Soon, it is dinner time. The grown-ups eat lots of bamboo shoots, crunching the juicy stems. Chi-li likes to chew the soft leaves.

The grown-ups eat for such a long time, they always fall asleep afterwards. Chi-li scampers off to play. He rolls over and over in the snow and tumbles down a hill.

When Chi-li stops at the bottom he cannot see his mother any more. But he sees a leopard! Chi-li is very frightened.

He scrambles over to the nearest tree and climbs up. Chi-li has never climbed before, and it is so easy! He digs his claws into the bark and goes up and up.

Soon, he is near the top. Chi-li feels so good up here. And he can see such a long way over the mountains and trees and snow of China.

Chi-li hears his mother crying. She is looking for him. He starts to climb down. But going down is harder than climbing up, and he slips. Plop! He lands in the snow.

Chi-li's mother is so happy. She gathers him up in her big furry arms and cuddles him. It is lovely to be warm and safe with her again.

FIVE MINUTES' PEACE

by Jill Murphy

The children were having breakfast. This was not a pleasant sight.
Mrs Large took a tray from the cupboard.
She set it with a teapot, a milk jug, her favourite cup and saucer, a plate of marmalade toast and a leftover cake from yesterday. She stuffed the morning paper into her pocket and sneaked off towards the door.
"Where are you going with that tray, Mum?" asked Laura.
"To the bathroom," said Mrs Large.

"Why?" asked the other two children.
"Because I want five minutes' peace from you lot," said Mrs Large.
"That's why."

"Can we come?" asked Lester as they trailed up the stairs behind her.
"No," said Mrs Large, "you can't."
"What shall we do then?" asked Laura.
"You can play," said Mrs Large.
"Downstairs. By yourselves. And keep an eye on the baby."
"I'm not a baby," muttered the little one.

Mrs Large ran a deep, hot bath. She emptied half a bottle of bath foam into the water, plonked on her bath-hat and got in.
She poured herself a cup of tea and lay back with her eyes closed.
It was heaven.

"Can I play you my tune?" asked Lester.

Mrs Large opened one eye.

"Must you?" she asked.

"I've been practising," said Lester. "You told me to. Can I? Please, just for one minute."

"Go on then," sighed Mrs Large.

So Lester played. He played "Twinkle, Twinkle, Little Star" three and a half times. In came Laura. "Can I read you a page from my reading book?" she asked.

"No, Laura," said Mrs Large. "Go on, all of you, off downstairs."

"You let Lester play his tune," said Laura. "I heard. You like him better than me. It's not fair."

"Go on then. Just one page."

So Laura read. She read four and a half pages of "Little Red Riding Hood".

In came the little one with a trunkful of toys. "For you!" he beamed, flinging them all into the bath water.

"Thank you, dear," said Mrs Large weakly.

"Can I see the cartoons in the paper?" asked Laura.

"Can I have the cake?" asked Lester.

"Can I get in with you?" asked the little one. Mrs Large groaned.

In the end they all got in. The little one was in such a hurry that he forgot to take off his pyjamas.

Mrs Large got out. She dried herself, put on her dressing-gown and headed for the door.

"Where are you going now, Mum?" asked Laura.

"To the kitchen," said Mrs Large.

"Why?" asked Lester.

"Because I want five minutes' peace from you lot," said Mrs Large. "That's why." And off she went downstairs, where she had three minutes and forty-five seconds of peace before they all came to join her.

15

Tell Us a Story

by Allan Ahlberg
illustrated by
Colin McNaughton

Two little boys
climbed up
to bed.

"Tell us a story, Dad,"
they said.
"Right!" said Dad.

The Pig

"There was once a pig
who ate too much
and got so big
he couldn't sit down,
he couldn't bend.

So he ate standing up
and got bigger –
The End!"

"That story's no good,
Dad," the little boys said.
"Tell us a better one
instead."
"Right!" said Dad.

The Cat

"There was once a cat
who ate so much
and got so fat

he split his fur
which he had to mend
with a sewing machine
and a zip – The End!"

"That story's too mad,
Dad," the little boys said.
"Tell us another one
instead."
"Right!" said Dad.

The Horse

There once was a horse who ate too much and died, of course – The End!"

He's not dead!

I'm just horsing around!

That story's too sad, Dad," the little boys said. 'Tell us a nicer one instead." 'Right!" said Dad.

The Cow

"There once was a cow who ate so much that even now she fills two fields

I've got four stomachs to fill!

and blocks a road, and when they milk her she has to be towed! She wins gold cups and medals too, for the creamiest milk and the *loudest* moo!"

"Now that's the end," said Dad. "No more." And he shut his eyes and began to snore.

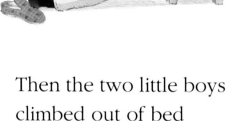

Then the two little boys climbed out of bed and crept downstairs

to their Mum instead.

The End

ROBERT

by Philippe

Robert lived with his mother and father in a big house. He had no brothers or sisters but he had lots of toys to play with. One day his mother came into his room. "Robert," she said, "be a little angel and run down to the shops for some biscuits. Aunt Susie is coming to tea."

On the way Robert met Mrs French. "Going shopping for your mummy?" she said. "What a good little boy you are."

At the flower stall the lady said, "That's Mrs Waters' little Robert. Isn't he a little darling?"

Mr Brown in the shop said, "Hello, little man. What can I do for you?"

"Little again!" Robert thought crossly. "Why do they all say I'm little?"

When Robert got home Aunt Susie was there.

"You little sweetie, my favourite biscuits!" she cooed. "Here, help yourself, my pet. I know what hungry tummies little boys like you always have."

"I am *not* little!" Robert screamed

I AM NOT LITTLE!!

THE GREAT

Dupasquier

furiously and he marched up to his room and slammed the door. From that moment on, Robert was a different boy. He was always staring into the mirror. "What rubbish," he'd say, "I'm not little. I'm *not*." He sulked. He did all kinds of silly things, trying to make himself look bigger.

Robert's behaviour got worse and worse. His parents were at their wits' end.

They tried everything. In the end they sent for the doctor. But that was no good. Robert bit him.

That night he dressed up as a horrible monster. "I'm a giant. I'm going to gobble you all up!" he shouted.

"This can't go on," said Mr Waters. "What the boy needs is a change."

So the next day they went on a trip to the zoo.

Robert was as horrid as ever. "I hate zoos," he said.

He hated the parrots; he hated the giraffes; he didn't even like the monkeys. Then a great big truck came into the zoo. On the truck was a cage and in the cage was an enormous tiger.

The keeper got up to check the bolts. "Keep back," he warned. "This fellow eats people for breakfast."

Just then a terrible thing happened. The tiger jumped at the cage door. The keeper fell over backwards. The door flew open.

The tiger leapt out. People were screaming and running everywhere. But Robert was left behind. He was standing in front of the cage. All by himself. Except for the tiger.

The tiger crouched, ready to spring. Someone screamed, "It's going to eat the little boy!"

But Robert had seen the open cage. The tiger pounced; Robert dashed inside. The tiger was right behind him. But before the tiger could reach him Robert squeezed out through the bars on the other side. No sooner had his feet touched the ground than he quickly ran round the truck. SLAM!

He had the cage door shut and bolted. The tiger was trapped.

The crowd couldn't believe it. Everyone cheered. Robert was a hero! They carried him round the zoo in triumph.

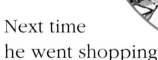

Next time he went shopping nobody called Robert little.

"My, what a big boy you are," Mrs French called as he passed.

"Stronger than a tiger," said the lady at the flower stall.

Everyone he met seemed to know about his great adventure.

"Here comes Robert the Great. Aren't we all proud of our big boy then?" said Aunt Susie the next time she came to tea.

"I'm not really big," Robert said, "or I couldn't have got through the bars of the cage, could I, Aunt Susie?"

TERRIBLE, TERRIBLE

There once was a terrible tiger, so terrible to see.
There once was a terrible tiger, as fierce as fierce can be.
There once was a terrible tiger that looked down from a tree.
There once was a terrible tiger that came creeping after me.
There once was a terrible tiger with teeth as sharp as sharp could be.
That terrible, terrible tiger – will he eat ME?
That terrible, terrible tiger, he roared … and leapt at me.

TIGER
by Colin and Jacqui Hawkins

I cuddled that terrible tiger.
He's really my kitten, you see.

DUCK

by David Lloyd

illustrations by Charlotte Voake

There was a time, long ago, when Tim called all animals duck.
"Duck," Tim said.
"Horse," said Granny.
"Duck," Tim said.
"Sheep," said Granny.
"Duck," Tim said.
"Speckled hen," said Granny.
So Granny took Tim to the pond.
"Duck," she said.
Tim looked and looked.
"Duck," he said.
Granny kissed him.

A little later
Tim saw a tractor.
"Truck," he said.
A little later
Tim saw a bus.
"Truck," he said.
A little later
Tim saw an old car.
"Truck," he said.
So Granny showed Tim a truck.
"Truck," she said.
Tim looked and looked.
"Truck," he said.
Granny kissed him.

For some time 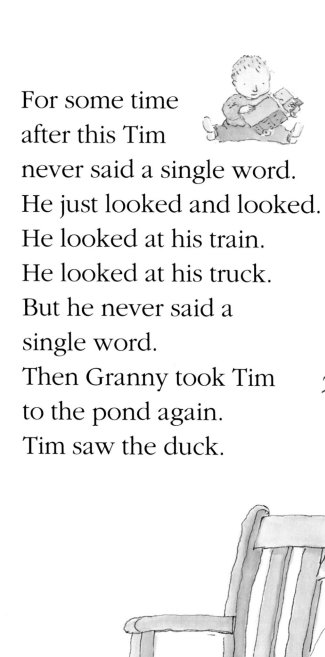 after this Tim never said a single word. He just looked and looked. He looked at his train. He looked at his truck. But he never said a single word. Then Granny took Tim to the pond again. Tim saw the duck.

He looked and looked. The duck said, "Quack!" "Duck," Tim said. "Duck," Granny said. Granny kissed Tim. Tim kissed Granny.

25

We Love Them

by Martin Waddell
illustrated by Barbara Firth

It lay with Ben. Ben licked it. Becky said that Ben thought it was a little dog, and it thought Ben was a big rabbit. They didn't know they'd got it wrong. Becky said we wouldn't tell them.

We called our rabbit Zoe. She stayed with Ben. She played with Ben.

We loved them.

Zoe wasn't little for very long. She got big... and bigger... and bigger still, but not as big as Ben.

But Ben was old... and one day Ben died. We were sad and Zoe was sad. She wouldn't eat her green stuff. She sat and sat.

In all the white fields there was one rabbit. It was lost. It was small. It lay in the snow.

Ben found it. Ben barked. We picked it up and took it home. Becky thought it would die, but it didn't.

There was no Ben for our rabbit, until one day… in the pale hay …there was a puppy.

We took it home. It lay down with Zoe. Becky said our puppy thought Zoe was a dog. And Zoe thought our puppy

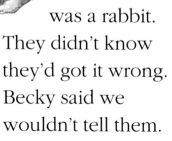

was a rabbit. They didn't know they'd got it wrong. Becky said we wouldn't tell them.

The puppy stayed. The puppy played. We loved him, just like we loved Ben.

We called our puppy Little Ben. But Little Ben got big… and bigger… and bigger

still. He got bigger than our rabbit but not as big as old Ben.

Zoe still thinks Little Ben is a rabbit, and Becky says that Zoe doesn't mind.

Becky says that Zoe likes big rabbits.

Zoe and little Ben play with us in the green fields. They are our dog and our rabbit.

We love them.

Out and About

by Shirley Hughes

The Grass House

The grass house
Is my private place.
Nobody can see me
In the grass house.
Feathery plumes
Meet over my head.
Down here,
In the green, there are:
Seeds
Weeds
Stalks
Pods
And tiny little flowers.

Only the cat
And some busy, hurrying ants
Know where my grass house is.

Mudlarks

I like mud.
The slippy, sloppy, squelchy kind,
The slap-it-into-pies kind.
Stir it up in puddles,
Slither and slide.
I *do* like mud.

Wind

I like the wind.
The soft, summery, gentle kind,
The gusty, blustery, fierce kind.
Ballooning out the curtains,
Blowing things about,
Wild and wilful everywhere.
I *do* like the wind.

Seaside

Sand in the sandwiches,
Sand in the tea,
Flat, wet sand running
Down to the sea.
Pools full of seaweed,
Shells and stones,
Damp bathing suits
And ice-cream cones.
Waves pouring in
To a sand-castle moat.
Mend the defences!
Now we're afloat!
Water's for splashing,
Sand is for play,
A day by the sea
Is the best kind of day.

Sand

I like sand.
The run-between-your-fingers kind,
The build-it-into-castles kind.
Mountains of sand meeting the sky,
Flat sand, going on for ever.
I *do* like sand.

Water

I like water.
The shallow, splashy, paddly kind,
The hold-on-tight-it's-deep kind.
Slosh it out of buckets,
Spray it all around.
I *do* like water.

Sick

Hot, cross, aching head,
Prickly, tickly, itchy bed.
Piles of books and toys and puzzles
Heavy on my feet,
Pillows thrown all anyhow,
Wrinkles in the sheet.
Sick of medicine, lemonade,
Soup spooned from a cup.
When will I be *better?*
When can I *get up?*

29

Beaky

by Jez Alborough

"I will call you Beaky. Come on, let's go for a walk."

"Am I a frog?" asked Beaky as they hopped along. Frog laughed. "If you were a frog," he said, "then you would be able to hop as high as me and you wouldn't have those funny fluffy flaps."

"If I'm not a frog," said Beaky, "then what am I?"

"I don't know," puzzled Frog, "I've never seen anything like you before; but you must be something…everything is something!"

Before long they found Snake. "What's he doing?" asked Beaky. "Slithering," said Frog. "Precisely," said Snake. "It's simply splendid to slither, you should try a slither yourself."

An egg tumbled down through the leaves and branches and shattered into pieces on the rain forest floor.

Out popped a fluffy creature with a bright blue beak and a curly orange tail.

"Hello," croaked Frog, jumping out from behind a bush.

"I'm a frog, what are you?" The creature looked confused.

"Don't you know what you are?" asked Frog. The creature shook its head.

"Then you can be my friend," said Frog.

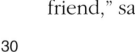

"Yes, have a try," said Frog, for he wondered whether Beaky might be some sort of snake. So Beaky lay on the earth and tried to slither. Nothing happened.
"Oh dear," said Frog. Snake laughed. "Too short," he said, and slithered off into the trees.
Beaky and Frog hopped to the river where they found Fish gliding about in the water.
"What's he doing?" asked Beaky.
"I'm swimming," said Fish. "Come and join me, the water's lovely."
"Good idea," said Frog, thinking that Beaky might be some sort of fish. "Try a swim."
Beaky splished and splashed and flipped and flapped, but couldn't swim a stroke. "Oh dear," said Frog. Fish giggled. "Too fluffy," he said, and swam away.
"Everyone knows what they are except me," sighed Beaky.
Just then he heard something singing softly, far away.
"Did you hear that?" he said excitedly. "Hear what?" said Frog.

"Listen!" said Beaky.
"It came from up there."
Frog looked up to the top of the trees, then he heard it too.
"Someone up there must be really happy," said Beaky, "to sing such a joyful song. Do you think I could ever be that happy?"
"Maybe," said Frog, "but not until we discover what you are." Then he had an idea.
"Let's climb up there," he said, "and see if we can find out."
So up they went, but the higher they climbed the more frightened Frog became. So Beaky had to go on alone. On and on he struggled, all through the day and into the night until he could go no further.

"Now I'm lost," cried Beaky, "and I still haven't found out what I am. Maybe I should never have left the forest floor. Perhaps the song was just a dream." And with this thought, he slept.

Beaky awoke the next morning to the sound of a familiar song. Looking round, he saw circling in the air a beautiful fluffy creature with a bright blue beak and a curly orange tail.

"What are you?" called Beaky.

"I'm a bird," sang the creature, "a bird of Paradise."

"A bird," said Beaky, "that's what I am."

In his excitement he jumped and skipped and dipped, he strutted, bobbed and trotted and then…

he tripped!

Down and down he fell, crashing through leaves and branches, down towards the earth below.

"Flap your wings!" called the bird. "Flap your wings!"

Beaky opened wide his fluffy flaps.

"My wings," he cried, "these are my *wings*." And with a *whoosh* he began to fly…up past a tree where Snake was slithering…down to the river where Fish was swimming…and back to the vine where Frog was still waiting.

"Frog," said Beaky, "look at me. I can't slither, or swim, or hop like you, but I can *fly!*"

At that moment Beaky heard the singing once more and it seemed to be calling him.

"I must go," he said, "but I'll come back and visit."

Then he flew up towards the treetops.

"Beaky," called Frog, "you haven't told me what you are."

"I'm a bird," cried Beaky. "I'm a bird...a bird of Paradise!"

Gregory Griggs,

Gregory Griggs,

Had twenty-seven different wigs.

He wore them up,

He wore them down,

To please the people of the town;

He wore them east,

He wore them west;

But he never could tell

Which he liked best.

Old Mother Shuttle

Lived in a coal-scuttle,

Along with her dog and her cat;

What they ate I can't tell,

But 'tis known very well,

That not one of the party was fat.

Old Mother Shuttle

Scoured out her coal-scuttle,

And washed both her dog and her cat;

The cat scratched her nose,

So they came to hard blows

And who was the gainer by that?

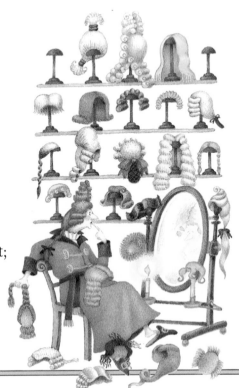

illustrated by Nicola Bayley

I dreamed a dream next Tuesday week,
Beneath the apple trees;
I thought my eyes were big pork pies,
  And my nose was Stilton cheese.
    The clock struck twenty minutes to six,
    When a frog sat on my knee;
    I asked him to lend me eighteen pence,
But he borrowed a shilling of me.

There was an old lady of Wales,
Who lived upon oysters and snails.
Upon growing a shell,
She exclaimed, "It is well,
I won't have to wear bonnets or veils."

MRS GOOSE'S

One day Mrs Goose found an egg and made a lovely nest to put it in. Mrs Goose sat on the egg to keep it safe and warm.
Soon the egg started

to crack open. The little bird inside was pecking at the shell.
Mrs Goose's baby was very very small and fluffy and yellow.
Mrs Goose took her baby out to eat some grass.
But her baby didn't want to eat grass. She ran off to look for something different.

Mrs Goose took her naughty baby to the pond.
The water looked cold and grey.
Poor Mrs Goose! Her baby would not swim!

BABY

by Charlotte Voake

The baby grew  and grew and grew.

Mrs Goose's feathers were smooth and white.

Mrs Goose's baby had untidy brown feathers.

Mrs Goose had large webbed feet.

Her baby had little pointed toes.

The baby followed Mrs

Goose everywhere,

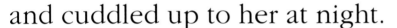 and cuddled up to her at night.

Mrs Goose guarded her

baby from strangers.

Mrs Goose's baby never did eat much grass.

The baby never did go swimming in the pond.

And everyone except Mrs Goose knew why.

Mrs Goose's baby was a
CHICKEN!

Sally and the Limpet

by Simon James

Not long ago, on a Sunday, Sally was down on the beach exploring, when she found a brightly coloured, bigger-than-usual limpet shell. She wanted to take it home but, as she pulled, the limpet made a little squelching noise and held on to the rock. The harder Sally tugged, the more tightly the limpet held on, until, suddenly, Sally slipped and fell – with the limpet stuck to her finger.

Though she pulled with all her might, it just wouldn't come off. So she ran over to her dad. He heaved and groaned, but the limpet made a little squelching noise and held on even tighter.

So, that afternoon, Sally went home in the car with a limpet stuck to her finger. When they got home, her dad tried using his tools.

Her brother tried offering it lettuce and cucumber.

But, that night, Sally went to bed with a limpet stuck to her finger.

Next day it was school. All her friends tried to pull the limpet off her finger.

Mr Wobblyman, the nature teacher, said that limpets live for twenty years, and stay all their lives on the same rock.

In the afternoon, Sally's mother took her to the hospital, to see the doctor. He tried chemicals, injections, potions and pinchers.

Sally was beginning to feel upset. Everyone was making too much fuss all around her. She kicked over the doctor's chair and ran. She ran through the endless corridors. She just wanted to be on her own. She ran out of the hospital and through the town. She didn't stop when she got to the beach. She ran through people's sandcastles. She even ran over a fat man.

When she reached the water, she jumped in with all her clothes on. Sally landed with a big splash and then just sat in the water.

The limpet, feeling at home once more, made a little squelching noise and wiggled off her finger.

But Sally didn't forget what Mr Wobblyman, the nature teacher, had said. Very carefully, she lifted the limpet by the top of its shell. She carried it back across the beach, past the fat man she had walked on, and gently, so gently, she put the limpet back on the very same rock where she had found it the day before.

Then, humming to herself, she took the long way home across the beach.

WHO'S  BEEN SLEEPING

I ONCE SAW A FISH UP A TREE

I once saw a fish up a tree,
  And this fish he had legs, believe me.
    Said the monster, "I'll swear,
    I'm just taking the air."
Then he jumped down and ran off to sea.

MUM IS HAVING A BABY!

Mum is having a baby!
I'm shocked! I'm all at sea!
What's she want another one for:
WHAT'S THE MATTER WITH ME!?

WHO'S BEEN SLEEPING IN MY PORRIDGE?

"Who's been sitting in my bed?"
  said the mummy bear crossly.
"Who's been eating my chair?"
  said the baby bear weepily.
"Who's been sleeping in my porridge?"
  said the papa bear angrily.
"Wait a minute," said Goldilocks.

"Why can't you guys just stick
  to the script? Now let's try
it again and this time no messing about."

IN MY PORRIDGE? *by Colin McNaughton*

ON YOUR HEAD BE IT!

If you're poor and in distress,
Without a bean and penniless,
Your head is cold, your bonce is blue,
Then this is my headvice to you:
Wear a teapot, wear a shoe,
Lift it up, say "How de do!"
Wear a sock, wear a pan,
Wear a king-size baked-bean can.
Wear a saucer, wear a cup,
Wear a plantpot, downside up.
Wear a bucket, wear a bowl,
Wear the tube from a toilet roll.
Wear a lampshade, wear a vase,
Wear a fishbowl, man from Mars!

Wear a pie (not too hot!),
Wear a sooty chimneypot.
Wear a matchbox, wear a book,
For that literary look.
Wear an eggcup, plain or spotty,
Wear a washed-out baby's potty.
Wear a yellow traffic cone,
Wear a big brass bass trombone.
Wear an orange rubber glove,
Wear a housetrained turtle-dove.
Wear a ball, a loaf of bread,
A ripe banana – use your head!
Your head's in the sand if you can't see it.
If you catch cold, ON YOUR HEAD BE IT!

THE CROCODILE'S BRUSHING HIS TEETH

The crocodile's brushing his teeth, I'm afraid,
This certainly means we're too late.
The crocodile's brushing his teeth, I'm afraid,
He has definitely put on some weight.
The crocodile's brushing his teeth, I'm afraid,
It really is, oh, such a bore.
The crocodile's brushing his teeth, I'm afraid,
He appears to have eaten class four!

41

THE HAPPY HEDGEHOG

Deep in the heart of Dickon Wood lived a happy hedgehog named Harry.

Harry loved noise so he made a big drum and he banged on the drum tum-tum-te-tum. A hedgehog called Helen was out in the wood. She heard tum-tum-te-tum and she liked it. So she made a drum and went off to join in the drumming. And so did a hedgehog named Norbert and another called Billy; they both made drums and followed the tum-tum-te-tums, until all of the hedgehogs with drums were gathered together at Harry's. Tum-tum-te-tum went one drum; that was Harry. Diddle-diddle-dum went

one drum; that was Helen. Ratta-tat-tat went one drum; that was Norbert. And BOOM went one drum; that was Billy. Tum-tum-te-tum diddle-diddle-dum ratta-tat-tat   BOOM Tum-tum-te-tum diddle-diddle-

BAND

by *Martin Waddell*   illustrated by *Jill Barton*

and the dove, the frog and the toad and the spider and the dog who was lost in the wood. Tum went the band and they STOPPED!

"We want to play too!" said the others. "But we haven't got drums. So what can we do?" And nobody knew except Harry.

dum ratta-tat-tat   BOOM
The whole wood was humming and tumming with drumming. **"STOP!"** cried the pheasant, the owl and the bee, the mole from his hole and a badger called Sam and his mother, and the fox and the crow, the deer

Harry knew all about noise. So he said, "You can hum, you can hoot, you can buzz, you can whistle, you can clap, you can click, you can pop. We'll carry on with the drums."

And ...

44

ba-zooo ba-zoooo

clack-clack

h-ka

ratta-tat-tat

diddle-diddle-diddle

dum

BOOM

they did.

And the dog
who was lost
in the wood
just danced.

Tum-tum-te-tum
diddle-diddle-dum
ratta-tat-tat

BOOM

A Little Boy Came

from
HARD-BOILED LEGS

by **Michael Rosen**   illustrated by **Quentin Blake**

A little boy came down to breakfast

with bananas stuck in his ears.

Everyone said hello to him

but he didn't take any notice.

So his mum said, "Are you all right?"

but the little boy said nothing.

So his sister said,

"Are you all right?"

but the little boy

still said nothing.

Then his brother noticed that

he had bananas stuck in his ears, so he said,

Down to Breakfast

"Hey, you've got bananas stuck in your ears," and the little boy said, "What?" So his brother said it again. "You've got bananas stuck in your ears," and the little boy said, "What?" So the brother shouted really loudly at him, "YOU'VE GOT BANANAS STUCK IN YOUR EARS!"

And the little boy shouted back, "I'M SORRY, I CAN'T HEAR YOU. I'VE GOT BANANAS IN MY EARS!"

47

Rhymes from **Over the**

On Saturday night I lost my wife,
And where do you think I found her?
Up in the moon, singing a tune,
And all the stars around her.

Sally go round the sun,
Sally go round the moon,
Sally go round the chimney-pots
On a Saturday afternoon.

Moon

illustrated by **Charlotte Voake**

Hey diddle, diddle,
The cat and the fiddle,
	The cow jumped over the moon.
The little dog laughed
To see such sport,
	And the dish ran away with the spoon.

The man in the moon
Came tumbling down,
	And asked his way to Norwich.
He went by the south,
And burnt his mouth
	With supping cold pease-porridge.

Daley B

Daley B didn't know
what he was.
"Am I a monkey?"
he said.
"Am I a koala?
Am I a porcupine?"

Daley B didn't know
where to live.
"Should I live in a cave?"
he said.
"Should I live in a nest?
Should I live in a web?"

Daley B didn't know
what to eat.
"Should I eat fish?"
he said.
"Should I eat potatoes?
Should I eat worms?"

Daley B didn't know
why his feet were so big.
"Are they for water
skiing?" he said.

"Are they for the mice
to sit on?
Are they to keep the
rain off?"

Daley B saw the birds
in the tree, and decided
he would live in a tree.
Daley B saw the
squirrels eating acorns,
and decided he would
eat acorns.
But he still didn't know
why his feet were so big.

One day, there was great
panic in the woodland.
All the rabbits gathered
beneath Daley B's tree.
"You must come down
at once, Daley B!"
they cried. "Jazzy D
is coming!"
"Who is Jazzy D?" asked
Daley B.

by Jon Blake *illustrated by* Axel Scheffler

The rabbits were too excited to answer. They scattered across the grass and vanished into their burrows. Daley B stayed in his tree, and nibbled another acorn, and wondered about his big feet.

Jazzy D crept out of the bushes. Her teeth were as sharp as broken glass, and her eyes were as quick as fleas. Jazzy D sneaked around the burrows, but there was not a rabbit to be seen.

Jazzy D looked up. Daley B waved. Jazzy D began to climb the tree. The other rabbits poked out their noses, and trembled.

51

"Hello," said Daley B to Jazzy D. "Are you a badger? Are you an elephant? Are you a duck-billed platypus?"

Jazzy D crept closer.

"No, my friend," she whispered. "I am a weasel."

"Do you live in a pond?" asked Daley B.

"Do you live in a dam? Do you live in a kennel?"

Jazzy D crept closer still.

"No, my friend," she hissed, "I live in the darkest corner of the wood."

"Do you eat cabbages?" asked Daley B. "Do you eat insects? Do you eat fruit?"

Jazzy D crept right up to Daley B.

"No, my friend," she rasped, "I eat rabbits! Rabbits like you!"

Daley B's face fell. "Am I ... a rabbit?" he stammered.

Jazzy D nodded ... and licked her lips ...

and **leapt!**

52

Daley B didn't have to think. Quick as a flash, he turned his back, and kicked out with his massive feet. Jazzy D sailed through the air, far far away, back where she came from.

The other rabbits jumped and cheered and hugged each other. "You're a hero, Daley B!" they cried.

"That's funny," said Daley B. "I thought I was a rabbit."

OWL BABIES

Once there were three baby owls:

Sarah…   and Percy…

and Bill.

They lived in a hole
in the trunk of a tree
with their Owl Mother.

The hole had twigs and
leaves and owl feathers in it.
It was their house.

BY MARTIN WADDELL   ILLUSTRATED BY PATRICK BENSON

One night they woke up and
their Owl Mother was GONE.
"Where's Mummy?" asked Sarah.
"Oh my goodness!" said Percy.
"I want my mummy!" said Bill.

The baby owls *thought*
(all owls think a lot) –
"I think she's gone hunting,"
said Sarah.
"To get us our food!" said Percy.
"I want my mummy!" said Bill.

But their Owl Mother didn't come.
The baby owls came out of their
house and they sat on the tree
and waited.

A big branch for Sarah,
a small branch for Percy,
and an old bit of ivy for Bill.
"She'll be back," said Sarah.
"Back *soon!*" said Percy.
"I want my mummy!" said Bill.

It was dark in the wood and
they had to be brave, for things
moved all around them.

"She'll bring us mice and things
that are nice," said Sarah.
"I suppose so!" said Percy.
"I want my mummy!" said Bill.

They sat and they thought
(all owls think a lot) –
"I think we should *all* sit on *my*
branch," said Sarah.
And they did, all three together.

"Suppose she got lost," said Sarah.
"Or a fox got her!" said Percy.
"I want my mummy!"
said Bill.
And the baby owls
closed their owl eyes
and wished their
Owl Mother
would come.

55

AND SHE CAME.
Soft and silent, she swooped
through the trees to Sarah and
Percy and Bill.
"Mummy!" they cried, and they
flapped and they danced, and they
bounced up and down on their
branch.
"WHAT'S ALL THE FUSS?"
their Owl Mother asked.
"You knew I'd come back."
The baby owls thought
(all owls think a lot) –
"I knew it," said Sarah.
"And I knew it!" said Percy.
"I love my mummy!"
    said Bill.

A Zoo in

Mum and I went to
the zoo.
I said, "Can I have a zoo
in our house?"
"Certainly not," said Mum.

But …

… on Monday a giraffe
was eating in
the kitchen.

On Tuesday
a hippopotamus was
splashing in the bath.

On Wednesday a monkey
was swinging in the hall.

On Thursday
a crocodile was washing
in the garden.

Our House

by Heather Eyles
illustrated by Andy Cooke

On Friday a lion
was sleeping in the
living room.

On Saturday all the
animals came and
we had a party.

On Sunday Mum
sent them all
back to
the zoo.

"Phew," said Mum.

But …

… she forgot
the gorilla.

Floss

by *Kim Lewis*

Floss was a young border collie, who belonged to an old man in a town. She walked with the old man in the streets, and loved playing ball with children in the park. "My son is a farmer," the old man told Floss. "He has a sheepdog who is too old to work. He needs a young dog to herd sheep on his farm. He could train a Border collie like you." So Floss and the old man travelled, away from the town with its streets and houses and children playing ball in the park. They came to the heather-covered hills of a valley, where nothing much grew except sheep. Somewhere in her memory, Floss knew about sheep. Old Nell soon showed her how to round them up. The farmer trained her to run wide and lie down, to walk on behind, to shed,

and to pen. She worked very hard to become a good sheepdog.

up balls in the park. The farmer took Floss on the hill one day, to see if she could gather the sheep on her own. She was rounding them up when she heard a sound. At the edge of the field the farmer's children were playing, with a brand new black and white ball.

Floss remembered all about children. She ran to play with their ball. She showed off her best nose kicks, her best passes. She did her best springs in the air.

"Hey, Dad, look at this!" yelled the children. "Look at Floss!"

But sometimes Floss woke up at night, while Nell lay sound asleep.

She remembered about playing with children and rounding

61

The sheep started drifting away. The sheep escaped through the gate and into the yard. There were sheep in the garden and sheep on the road. "FLOSS! LIE DOWN!" The farmer's voice was like thunder.

"You are meant for work on this farm, not play!" He took Floss back to the dog house. Floss lay and worried about balls and sheep. She dreamt about the streets of a town, the hills of a valley, children and farmers, all mixed together, while Nell had to round up the straying sheep. But Nell was too

old to work every day, and Floss had to learn to take her place. She worked so hard to gather sheep well, she was much too tired to dream

any more. The farmer was pleased and ran Floss in the dog trials. "She's a good worker now," the old man said. The children still wanted

to play with their ball. "Hey, Dad," they asked, "can Old Nell play now?" But Nell didn't know about children and play. "No one can play ball like Floss," they said. "Go on, then," whispered the farmer to Floss. The children kicked the ball high in the air. Floss remembered all about children. She ran to play with their ball. She showed off her best nose kicks, her best passes. She did her best springs in the air.

TEN IN THE BED

There were **TEN** in the bed
and the little one said,
"Roll over, roll over!"
So they all rolled over
and Hedgehog fell out …

BUMP!

There were **NINE** in the bed
and the little one said,
"Roll over, roll over!"
So they all rolled over
and Zebra fell out …

OUCH!

There were **EIGHT** in the bed
and the little one said,
"Roll over, roll over!"
So they all rolled over
and Ted fell out …

THUMP!

There were **SEVEN** in the bed
and the little one said,
"Roll over, roll over!"
So they all rolled over
and Croc fell out …

THUD !

There were **SIX** in the bed
and the little one said,
"Roll over, roll over!"
So they all rolled over
and Rabbit fell out …

BONK!

There were **FIVE** in the bed
and the little one said,
"Roll over, roll over!"
So they all rolled over
and Mouse fell out …

DINK!

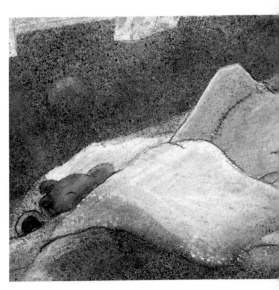

by Penny Dale

There were **FOUR** in the bed
and the little one said,
"Roll over, roll over!"
So they all rolled over
and Nelly fell out …

CRASH!

There were **THREE** in the bed
and the little one said,
"Roll over, roll over!"
So they all rolled over
and Bear fell out …

SLAM!

There were **TWO** in the bed
and the little one said,
"Roll over, roll over!"
So they all rolled over
and Sheep fell out …

DONK!

There was **ONE** in the bed
and the little one said,
"I'm cold! I miss you!"

So they all came back
and jumped into bed –
Hedgehog, Mouse, Nelly, Zebra,
Ted, the little one, Rabbit, Croc,
Bear and Sheep.

Ten in the bed,
all fast asleep.

A Piece of Cake

by Jill Murphy

"I'm fat," said Mrs Large. "No you're not," said Lester. "You're our cuddly mummy," said Laura. "You're just right," said Luke. "Mummy's got wobbly bits," said the baby. "Exactly," said Mrs Large. "As I was saying – I'm fat."

"We must all go on a diet," said Mrs Large. "No more cakes. No more biscuits. No more crisps. No more sitting around all day. From now on, it's healthy living."

"Can we watch TV?" asked Lester, as they trooped in from school. "Certainly not!" said Mrs Large. "We're all off for a nice healthy jog round the park." And they were.

"What's for tea, Mum?" asked Laura when they arrived home.

"Some nice healthy watercress soup," said Mrs Large. "Followed by a nice healthy cup of water." "Oh!" said Laura. "That sounds ... nice."

"I'm just going to watch the news, dear," said Mr Large when he came home from work. "No you're not, dear," said Mrs Large. "You're off for a nice healthy jog round the park, followed by your tea – a delicious sardine with grated carrot." "I can't wait," said Mr Large.

It was awful. Every morning there was a healthy breakfast followed by exercises. Then there was a healthy tea followed by a healthy jog. By the time evening came everyone felt terrible. "We aren't getting any thinner, dear," said Mr Large.

"Perhaps elephants are meant to be fat," said Luke. "Nonsense!" said Mrs Large. "We mustn't give up now." "Wibbly-wobbly, wibbly-wobbly," went the baby.

One morning a parcel arrived. It was a cake from Granny. Everyone stared at it hopefully. Mrs Large put it into the cupboard on a high shelf. "Just in case we have visitors," she said sternly.

Everyone kept thinking about the cake. They thought about it during tea. They thought about it during the healthy jog. They thought about it in bed that night. Mrs Large sat up. "I can't stand it any more," she said to herself. "I must have a piece of that cake."

66

Mrs Large crept out of bed and went downstairs to the kitchen. She took a knife out of the drawer and opened the cupboard. There was only one piece of cake left!

"Ah ha!" said Mr Large, seeing the knife. "Caught in the act!"

Mrs Large switched on the light and saw Mr Large and all the children hiding under the table.

"There *is* one piece left," said Laura in a helpful way.

Mrs Large began to laugh. "We're all as bad as each other!" she said, eating the last piece of cake before anyone else did. "I do think elephants are meant to be fat," said Luke.

"I think you're probably right, dear," said Mrs Large. "Wibbly-wobbly, wibbly-wobbly!" went the baby.

HORATIO'S BED

All night Horatio could not sleep.

He tossed
and turned,

and wriggled,
and rolled.

But he just could not
get comfortable.
I'll go and ask James
what's the matter,
he thought.
James was
busy drawing.
Horatio sat down.
"I couldn't sleep
all night," he said.
"Is it your bed?"
asked James.
"I haven't got
a bed," Horatio said.

"Then let's make you one,"
said James.
James took a clean sheet of paper
from his Useful Box and very
carefully drew a bed for Horatio.

by Camilla Ashforth

It was a big square bed with a leg at each corner. Then he took another sheet of paper and drew another bed for Horatio. This one was a big square bed with a leg at each corner too.

Horatio was very excited. He took one of James's drawings and tried to fold it into a bed. Then he climbed inside it and closed his eyes.

It wasn't very comfortable and when Horatio rolled over …

R R R I I I P P P !

James looked up. "That bed looks too hard to sleep on," he said and carried on with his drawing.

Horatio thought for a moment. Then he pulled some feathers out of James's pillow and made a big square bed with them.

But when he lay on it the feathers tickled his nose.

AAACHOO! AAACHOO! AAACHOO!

He sneezed and sneezed.

James put down his pencil and
blew away the feathers.
James sat Horatio down on
his Useful Box.
"You wait here a minute," he said,
"while I just finish drawing your
bed." He had already drawn five
square beds and was getting
rather good at them.
But when James turned away,
Horatio slipped down from the
Useful Box. He wanted to see
what James kept inside.
He made some steps up to the lid.
He pushed it open and leaned in.
There were all sorts of things –
buttons, brushes, keys and
clothes pegs, clock wheels,
clips and little bits of string.
Horatio looked for a bed.
He couldn't find anything that
looked like James's drawings.

But he did find a big red sock.
"Look, James!" he cried.
"I've found your other sock!"
James did not seem very pleased.
He didn't like anyone looking in
his Useful Box. Not even Horatio.
Very quietly and carefully he
started to put away his Useful Bits.
When he had finished, he closed
the lid and looked for Horatio.
"Now we can make you
a bed," he said.

But there was no need, because
Horatio was fast asleep.
His bed was not
square and it did
not have a leg
at each corner.

But for little Horatio
it was just right.

BEARS IN THE FOREST

by Karen Wallace illustrated by Barbara Firth

Deep in a cave, a mother bear sleeps. She is huge and warm. Her heart beats slowly. Outside it is cold and the trees are covered in snow. Her newborn cubs are blind and tiny. They find her milk and begin to grow.

Snow slips from the trees and melts on the ground. The ice has broken on the lake. Mother bear wakes. Her long sleep is over. She leads her cubs down to the lake shore. She slurps and slurps the freezing water.

Leaves burst from their buds. There are frogs' eggs in the lake. Mother bear snuffs the air for strange smells, listens for strange sounds. Her cubs know nothing of the forest. This is their first spring. Mother bear must take care.

The summer sun is hot. Mother bear sits in a tree stump. Angry bees buzz around her head, and stolen honey drops from her paws.

Her two skinny bear cubs wrestle in the long grass. They squeal like little boys and roll over and over away from their mother. Mother bear growls.

Come back! There are dangers in the forest! Her cubs do not hear her. Mother bear snorts. She is angry. She strides across the meadow and whacks them with a heavy paw.

Two frightened bear cubs scramble up the nearest tree. Mother bear waits below, still as a statue, listening to the forest. When she feels safe, she will call her cubs down. Mother bear must take care.

Soon the days grow shorter and squirrels start to hide acorns. Bushes are bright with berries. Seed pods flutter to the ground. Winter is coming. Mother bear and her cubs eat everything they can find.

Icy winds blast the forest. Mother bear plods through the snow. Her cubs are fat. Their fur is thick. She chooses a shelter that is dark and dry, where they will sleep through the long winter months. When spring has woken the bears again, mother bear leads her cubs to

the river. She follows a trail worn deep in the ground. Hundreds of bears have walked this way before her. The river runs deep and fast. Mother bear wades in. Soon a silver trout flashes in her jaws. The cubs are hungry. They wade into the river and catch their own fish.

Mother bear gobbles berries. Her cubs are playing where she can't see them. They are almost grown. Soon they will leave her. Mother bear has taught them everything she knows.

The Owl and the Pussy Cat

Illustrated by Louise Voce   Written by Edward Lear

The Owl and
  the Pussy Cat
  went to sea
In a beautiful
  pea-green boat,
They took some honey,
  and plenty of money,
Wrapped up in a
  five-pound note.
The Owl looked up
  to the stars above,
And sang
  to a small guitar,
"O lovely Pussy!
  O Pussy, my love,
What a beautiful
  Pussy you are,
You are, you are!
What a beautiful
  Pussy you are!"

Pussy said to the Owl,
  "You elegant fowl!
How charmingly
  sweet you sing!
O let us be married!
  too long we have
  tarried:
But what shall we
  do for a ring?"

They sailed away,

for a year and a day,

To the land where

the Bong Tree grows,

And there in a wood
  a Piggy-wig stood
With a ring
  at the end of his nose,
His nose, his nose,
With a ring at the end
  of his nose.

"Dear Pig,
  are you willing
  to sell for one shilling
Your ring?"
  Said the Piggy, "I will."
So they took it away,
  and were married
  next day
By the Turkey
  who lives on the hill.

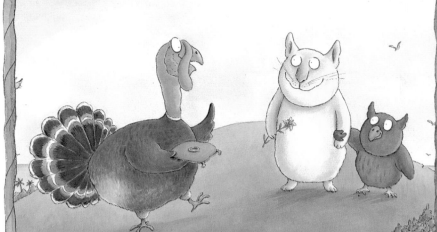

They dined on mince,
  and slices of quince,
Which they ate
  with a runcible spoon;
And hand in hand, on
  the edge of the sand,
They danced by the light
  of the moon,
The moon, the moon,
They danced by the light
  of the moon.

77

Let's Go Home, Little Bear

by Martin Waddell ✳ *illustrated by* Barbara Firth

Once there were two bears. Big Bear and Little Bear. Big Bear is the big bear and Little Bear is the little bear.

They went for a walk in the woods. They walked and they walked and they walked until Big Bear said, "Let's go home, Little Bear."

So they started back home on the path through the woods.

PLOD PLOD PLOD went Big Bear, plodding along.

Little Bear ran on in front, jumping and sliding and having great fun.

And then … Little Bear stopped and he listened and then he turned round and he looked.

"Come on, Little Bear," said Big Bear, but Little Bear didn't stir.

"I thought I heard something!" Little Bear said.

"What did you hear?" said Big Bear.

"Plod, plod, plod," said Little Bear. "I think it's a Plodder!"

Big Bear turned round and he listened and looked.

No Plodder was there.

"Let's go home, Little Bear," said Big Bear. "The plod was my feet in the snow."

They set off again on the path through the woods.

PLOD PLOD PLOD went Big Bear with Little Bear walking beside him, just glancing a bit, now and again.

And then … Little Bear stopped and he listened and then he turned round and he looked.

"Come on, Little Bear," said Big Bear, but Little Bear didn't stir.

"I thought I heard something!" Little Bear said.

"What did you hear?" said Big Bear.

"Drip, drip, drip," said Little Bear. "I think it's a Dripper!"

Big Bear turned round, and he listened and looked.

No Dripper was there.

"Let's go home, Little Bear," said Big Bear.

"That was the ice as it dripped in the stream."

They set off again on the path through the woods.

PLOD PLOD PLOD went Big Bear with Little Bear closer beside him.

And then … Little Bear stopped and he listened and then he turned round and he looked.

"Come on, Little Bear," said Big Bear, but Little Bear didn't stir.

"I know I heard something this time!" Little Bear said.

"What did you hear?" said Big Bear.

"Plop, plop, plop," said Little Bear. "I think it's a Plopper."

Big Bear turned round, and he listened and looked.

No Plopper was there.

"Let's go home, Little Bear," said Big Bear.

"That was the snow plopping down from a branch."

PLOD PLOD PLOD went Big Bear along the path through the woods. But Little Bear walked slower and slower and at last he sat down in the snow.

"Come on, Little Bear," said Big Bear. "It is time we were both back home."

But Little Bear sat and said nothing.

"Come on and be carried," said Big Bear.

Big Bear put Little Bear high up on his back, and set off down the path through the woods.

WOO WOO WOO "It's only the wind, Little Bear," said Big Bear and he walked on down the path.

CREAK CREAK CREAK "It's only the trees, Little Bear," said Big Bear and he walked on down the path.

PLOD PLOD PLOD "It is only the sound of my feet again," said Big Bear, and he plodded on and on and on until they came back home to their cave.

Big Bear and Little Bear went down into the dark, the dark of their own Bear Cave.

"Just stay there, Little Bear," said Big Bear, putting Little Bear in the Bear Chair with a blanket to keep him warm. Big Bear stirred up the fire from the embers and lighted the lamps and made the Bear Cave all cosy again.

"Now tell me a story," Little Bear said.

And Big Bear sat down in the Bear Chair with Little Bear curled on his lap. And he told a story of Plodders and Drippers and Ploppers and the sounds of the snow in the woods, and this Little Bear and this Big Bear plodding all the way...

HOME.

UNDER THE BED

by Michael Rosen   illustrated by Quentin Blake

Messing About

"Do you know what?"
said Jumping John.
"I had a bellyache
and now it's gone."

"Do you know what?"
said Kicking Kirsty.
"All this jumping
has made me thirsty."

"Do you know what?"
said Mad Mickey.
"I sat in some glue
and I feel all sticky."

"Do you know what?"
said Fat Fred.
"You can't see me,
I'm under the bed."

After Dark

Outside after dark
trains hum and traffic lights wink
after dark, after dark.

In here after dark
curtains shake and cupboards creak
after dark, after dark.

Under the covers after dark
I twiddle my toes and hug my pillow
after dark, after dark.

These Two Children

There were these two children
and they were in bed and it was
time they were asleep.

But they were making a huge noise,
shouting, yelling and screaming.
"Look at me!" "Look at you!"
"Let's go mad!" "Yes, let's go mad!"

Their dad heard them and
he shouted up to them,
"Stop the noise! Stop the noise!
If you don't stop the noise, I'm
coming upstairs and I'll give
you a bit of real trouble."

Everything went quiet.

A few minutes later one of the
children called out,
"Dad, Dad, when you come up to give
us a bit of real trouble, can you bring
us up a drink of water as well?"

Nat and Anna

Anna was in her room.
Nat was outside the door.
Anna didn't want Nat to come in.
Nat said, "Anna? Anna? Can I come in?"
Anna said, "I'm not in."

Nat went away.
Anna was still in her room.
Nat came back.
Nat said, "How did you say you're not in?
You must be in if you said you're not in."
Anna said, "I'm not in."
Nat said, "I'm coming in to see if you're in."
Anna said, "You won't find me because I'm not in."
Nat said, "I'm coming in."

Nat went in.
Nat said, "There you are. You are in."
Anna said, "Nat, where are you?
Where are you, Nat?"
Nat said, "I'm here."
Anna said, "I can't see you, Nat. Where are you?"
Nat said, "I'm here. Look."
Anna said, "Sorry, Nat. I can't see you."
Nat said, "Here I am. I'm going to scream, Anna.
Then you'll see me."
Anna said, "Where are you, Nat?"
Nat said, *"Yaaaaaaaaaaaaaaaaaaaa!"*
Anna said, "I can hear you, Nat. But I can't see you."
Nat said, "Right. I'm going out. Then you'll see me."

Nat went out.
Nat said, "Anna? Anna, can you see me now?"
Anna said, "No, of course I can't, you're outside."
Nat said, "Can I come in and see you then?"
Anna said, "But I'm not in."
Nat went away screaming.
He didn't come back.

83

In The Middle Of The Night

by Kathy Henderson

illustrated by Jennifer Eachus

A long time after bedtime
when it's very very late
when even dogs dream
and there's deep sleep
breathing through the house

when the doors are locked
and the curtains drawn
and the shops are dark
and the last train's gone
and there's no more traffic
    in the street
because everyone's asleep

then

the window-cleaner comes
to the high-street shop fronts
and shines at the glass
in the street-lit dark

and a dust-cart rumbles past
on its way to the dump
loaded with the last
of the old day's rubbish.

On the twentieth floor
of the office-block
there's a lighted window
and high up there
another night cleaner's
vacuuming the floor
working nights on her own
while her children sleep at home.

And down in the dome
    of the observatory
the astronomer who's
    waited all day
    for the dark

is watching the good black sky
    at last
for stars and moons
and spikes of light
through her telescope
in the middle of the night
while everybody sleeps.

At the bakery
the bakers in their floury clothes
mix dough in machines
for tomorrow's loaves of bread

and out by the gate
rows of parked vans wait
for their drivers to come
and take the newly-baked
bread to the shops
for the time when the
bread-eaters wake.

Across the town at the hospital
where the nurses watch in the
    dim-lit wards
someone very old shuts their eyes
and dies
breathes their very last breath
on their very last night.

Yet not far away on another floor
after months of waiting
a new baby's born
and the mother and the father
hold the baby and smile
and the baby looks up
and the world's just begun
but still everybody sleeps.

Now through the silent station
past the empty shops

and the office-blocks
past the sleeping streets
and the hospital
a train with no windows
goes rattling by

and inside the train the sorters sift
urgent letters and packets on the
    late night-shift
so tomorrow's post will arrive
    in time
at the towns and the villages
    down the line.

And the mother
with the wakeful child in her arms
walking up and down
and up and down
and up and down
the room
hears the train as it passes by
and the cats by the bins
and the night owl's flight
and hums hushabye and hushabye
we should be asleep now
you and I
it's late and time to close your eyes

it's the middle of the night.

singing

Giving
by Shirley Hughes

waving

I gave Mum a present on her birthday, all wrapped up in pretty paper. And she gave me a big kiss.
I gave Dad a very special picture which I painted at playgroup. And he gave me a ride on his shoulders most of the way home.

sleeping

telling

listening

thinking

kicking

eating

skipping

dancing

washing

smelling

I gave the baby some
slices of my apple.
We ate them sitting
under the table.
At teatime the baby
gave me two of his
soggy crusts.
That wasn't much of a present!
You can give someone a cross look
or a big smile! You can give a tea party
or a seat on a crowded bus.

yawning

stroking

giving

writing

tearing

singing

shouting

giving

crying

waving

On my birthday Grandma and Grandpa gave me
a beautiful doll's pram. I said "Thank you"
and gave them each a big hug.
And I gave my dear Bemily a ride
in it, all the way down the garden
path and back again.
I tried to give
the cat a ride
too, but she
gave me a
nasty scratch!

sleeping

telling

listening

thinking

kicking

eating

skipping

dancing

washing

smelling

So Dad had to give my poor arm a kiss and
a wash and a piece of sticking plaster.
Sometimes, just when I've
built a big castle out of
bricks, the baby
comes along and
gives it a big swipe!
And it all falls down.
Then I feel like giving
the baby a big swipe too. But I don't,
because he is my baby brother, after all.

yawning

stroking

giving

writing

tearing

89

THE MOST OBEDIENT DOG

The most obedient dog in the world was waiting for something to happen, when Harry came up the path.

"Hello, boy," said Harry.

The most obedient dog in the world wagged his tail and started to follow.

"No … sit!" said Harry.

"I won't be long."

And then he was gone.

"Why are you sitting there?" asked a nosy bird. "Are you going to sit there all day?"

The most obedient dog in the world didn't answer. He just sat and waited for Harry.

Big, fat raindrops began to fall.

"I'm off," said the bird. And he flew away.

Everyone ran for cover, except the most obedient dog in the world. Thunder rumbled, lightning flashed and then the hailstones fell…

Quite a lot of hailstones! When the sun came out again the bird flew back. The most obedient dog in the world was still sitting there waiting for Harry.

IN THE WORLD by Anita Jeram

"What a strange dog," people said as they passed. Other dogs came to have a look. They sniffed and nuzzled and nudged and nipped, but they soon got bored and went away. The most obedient dog in the world sat … and sat … and sat … and sat. How long must he wait for Harry? Just then, a cat came by. "Quick!" said the bird, pulling his tail. "Why don't you chase it?" The dog's eyes followed the cat. His nose started to twitch, and his legs started to itch. He couldn't sit still any longer. He sprang to his feet …

and saw Harry! "Good boy!" said Harry. "You waited! Leave that cat. Let's go to the beach!" The dog looked at the cat, and he looked at Harry. Then he went to the beach with Harry. After all, he was …

the most obedient dog in the world!

PARROT CAT

by Nicola Bayley

If I were a parrot
instead of a cat,

I would live
in the jungle,

I would fly
through the trees,

I would be coloured
so bright,

I would sit
on my nest,

I would talk
and squawk,

and if a snake
ever came,

I would quickly turn
back into a cat again.

FARMER DUCK

*by **Martin Waddell** illustrated by **Helen Oxenbury***

There once was a duck who had the bad luck to live with a lazy old farmer. The duck did the work. The farmer stayed all day in bed. The duck fetched the cow from the field.

"How goes the work?" called the farmer.

The duck answered,

"Quack!"

The duck brought the sheep from the hill.

"How goes the work?" called the farmer.

The duck answered, **"Quack!"**

The duck put the hens in their house.

"How goes the work?" called the farmer.

The duck answered, **"Quack!"**

The farmer got fat through staying in bed and the poor duck got fed up with working all day.

"How goes the work?" **"Quack!"**

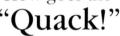

"How goes the work?"
"Quack!"

"How goes the work?"
"Quack!"

The poor duck was
sleepy and weepy
and tired.
The hens and
the cow and the
sheep got very upset.
They loved the duck.
So they held a meeting under the
moon and they made a plan for the
morning.

"How goes the work?"
"Quack!"

"How goes the work?"
"Quack!"

"How goes the work?"
"Quack!"

"Moo!" said the cow.
"Baa!" said the sheep.
"Cluck!" said the hens.

And *that* was the plan!

It was just before dawn
and the farmyard was still. Through
the back door and into the house crept
the cow and the sheep and the hens.

They stole down the hall.
They creaked up the stairs.
They squeezed under
the bed of the farmer
and wriggled about.
The bed started to rock
and the farmer woke up,
and he called,
"How goes the work?" and...

"M o o!"
"B a a!"
"C l u c k!"

They lifted his bed
and he started to shout, and
they banged and they bounced
the old farmer about and about and
about, right out of the bed ...
and he fled with the cow and the
sheep and the hens mooing and
baaing and clucking around him.

96

The duck awoke and waddled wearily into the yard expecting to hear, "How goes the work?" But nobody spoke!

Then the cow and the sheep and the hens came back.

"Quack?" asked the duck.

"Moo!" said the cow.

"Baa!" said the sheep.

"Cluck!" said the hens.

Which told the duck the whole story.

Then mooing and baaing and clucking and quacking they all set to work on their farm.

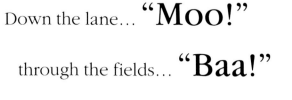

Down the lane... **"Moo!"** through the fields... **"Baa!"** over the hill... **"Cluck!"** and he never came back.

The FIBBS

by Chris Riddell

"Did you get the bananas?" asked Mrs Fibb

when Mr Fibb got back from the shops.

"Well, no," said Mr Fibb. "I meant to, but…"

"But what?" said Mrs Fibb.

"You're never going to believe this," said Mr Fibb,

"but I had just come out of the greengrocer's …

when a giant hairy hand came down from the sky and grabbed me! There I was on top of an office block in the clutches of a giant gorilla. I could see police cars and fire engines down below, and a huge crowd gathered. Then from out of the clouds came fighter planes with their guns blazing and the gorilla got very angry. So before there was a nasty accident I decided to sort things out myself. 'Excuse me,' I said to the gorilla, 'would you care for a banana?'

'How kind,' said the gorilla and ate all the bananas in one mouthful. Then he gave me a lift home on his back. Still, never mind, we can have some of your chocolate cake instead."

"Well, no," said Mrs Fibb. "I was baking today, but..."

"But what?" said Mr Fibb.

"*You're never going to believe this,*" said Mrs Fibb, "but just after you left, something that looked like a giant tea saucer landed in the back garden.

And three little green people climbed
out of it and came into the kitchen.
'We come in peace, earth woman,' they said.
'What's cooking?'
'Nothing yet,' I said, 'but I'm
about to bake a chocolate cake.'
'Then we shall help you,' they said and straight away they began.
They mixed up flour and baked beans and washing-up liquid and
pepper and put it in the oven. Before you could say 'little green

Martians' the oven door opened
and a big spongy blob
jumped out and started
chasing the cat.
'That's the best cake
we've ever baked,' said
the little green people.
'You can keep it if you like.'
'No, thank you,' I said.
'I like earth cooking much
better.' So then I baked them
a big chocolate cake.

When they had all tasted a piece, they said,
'You must give us the recipe, earth woman.'
'Only if you take that nasty blob with you
when you go,' I replied. So they did. And they
took the rest of the chocolate cake, I'm afraid.
Still, never mind, at least we can have a cup of tea.
Now where's the teapot?"

"You're never going to believe this,"
said Tommy Fibb, running into the room, "but…"
"But what?" said Mr and Mrs Fibb.
"Well," said Tommy Fibb, "Mrs McBean
from next door accidentally kicked her football
through the window this morning … and it landed on the
table and smashed the teapot. I meant to tell you earlier, but..."
"You can't believe a word that child says," said Mrs Fibb.
"I don't know where he gets it from,"
said Mr Fibb.

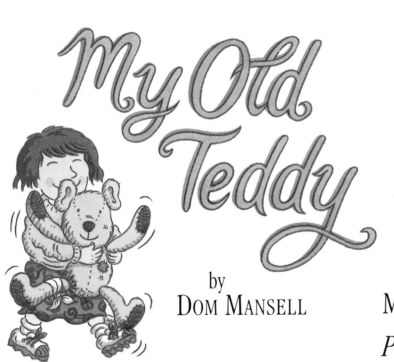

My Old Teddy

by
DOM MANSELL

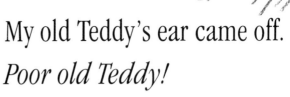

My old Teddy's leg came off.
Poor old Teddy!
I took him to the Teddy doctor.
She made Teddy better.

My old Teddy's ear came off.
Poor old Teddy!
I took him to the Teddy doctor.
She made Teddy better.

My old Teddy's
arm came off.
*Poor old
Teddy!*

I took him to the Teddy doctor.
She made Teddy better.

Then poor old Teddy's head
came off.

The Teddy doctor said, "Teddy's had enough now. Teddy has to rest."

The Teddy doctor gave me … my new Teddy. I love new Teddy very much, but I love poor old Teddy best.

Dear old, *poor old* Teddy.

Little Pig's Tale

by
Nigel Gray

illustrated by
Mary Rees

On Monday, Little Pig's dad told him, "Next Sunday, it's your mum's birthday."

"Will she have a party?" asked Little Pig.

"No. I don't think she'll have a party," said Dad.

"Will she have a birthday cake with lots of candles?"

"No. I don't think she'll want a cake with lots of candles."

"Will we sing *Happy Birthday to You?*"

"Yes. We must sing *Happy Birthday to You.*"

"And will we give her presents?"

"Of course," said Dad. "I'll give her a present. And you should give her a present too."

"What will I give her?" asked Little Pig.

"I don't know," said Dad. "You'll have to think of something."

On Tuesday, Little Pig tried to think of something exciting. Perhaps his mum would like an aeroplane so she could fly high, high above the town … or a rocket so she could explore the moon … or a spaceship so she could venture into outer space… But Little Pig knew he couldn't really give her a spaceship, or a rocket, or even an aeroplane. For one thing, their garage was too small. He'd have to think of something else.

On Wednesday, Little Pig thought of flowers and fruit. He'd give his mum an orchard – an orchard with pears and plums, apples and apricots, with daffodils and crocuses growing in the lush grass under the trees. He knew she'd like that because she was always weeding her window box, and growing plants in pots from apple pips and cherry stones.

Little Pig went to see Mr Green, the gardener. "I'm sure your mum would love an orchard," said Mr Green, "but your back yard is too small, and trees take years to grow. It was a good idea, Little Pig, but I'm afraid you'll have to think of something else."

On Thursday, Little Pig knew what he had to do. He raided his piggy bank and took his pennies to the shop.

He would buy his mum a silk gown, and a warm coat, and shiny shoes, and furry gloves, and glittering jewels for her to wear around her neck.

But the shopkeeper counted Little Pig's pennies and said, "I'm sorry, Little Pig, but you don't have enough money for any of those things."

"Not even for the gloves?" asked Little Pig.

"Not even for one glove," said the shopkeeper.

On Friday, Little Pig felt sad. In two days it would be his mum's birthday and Little Pig had nothing to give her. What was he to do?

He asked his dad.

"Why don't you make her something?" suggested Dad.

So Little Pig set to work.

He'd make her a useful box for keeping things in.

He fetched the tools, and found some old pieces of wood in the shed. The wood splintered. The box broke.

He'd make her a beautiful necklace of beads. He got the beads from the odds and ends drawer, and threaded the beads on cotton. The cotton snapped and the beads spilled all over the floor.

He'd do a painting in rainbow colours.

He got out the paints and a large sheet of white paper. But he knocked over the pot of black paint and spoiled his painting with an ugly blot.

He'd bake some cakes.

He mixed up flour and milk and eggs and sultanas and dates, and greased the baking tray with margarine. But the cakes burnt and came out of the oven as hard as stones.

On Saturday, Little Pig was in despair. He thought and thought until his brain hurt.

And then he had a brain wave.

He gathered together the things he would need.

A piece of paper, a pen and a red ribbon.

On Sunday, it was Little Pig's mum's birthday. After breakfast Little Pig and Dad sang *Happy Birthday to You*. Then Dad gave Mum a present… and while no one was looking, Little Pig slipped away.

Mum unwrapped her packet. Inside was a watch.

"That's because I want you to have a good time," Dad said. And Mum gave Dad a kiss.

Then, on the table, Mum found a note. It said:

To Mum.

Your present is upstairs in your bed. Happy Birthday! Lots of love from Little Pig.

Mum went up to the bedroom. There was certainly something in the bed. She pulled back the covers and there was…

Little Pig, with a red ribbon tied around him in a bow. "Happy Birthday, Mum!" said Little Pig.

"Oh, Little Pig," said Mum, "this is the best present you could possibly have given me. There's nothing in the world I'd rather have."

Mum hugged Little Pig and gave him a big sloppy kiss. And Little Pig beamed from ear to ear.

Noah's Ark

A long time ago there lived a man called Noah.

Noah was a good man, who trusted in God.

There were also many wicked people in the world.

God wanted to punish the wicked people,

so he said to Noah…

I shall make a flood of water and wash all the wicked people away. Build an ark for your family and all the animals.

Noah worked for years and years and years to build the ark.

At last the ark was finished.

Noah and his family gathered lots of food.

Then the animals came,

two by two,

two by two,

into the ark.

by Lucy Cousins

When the ark was full Noah felt a drop of rain. It rained and rained and rained. It rained for forty days and forty nights. The world was covered with water. At last the rain stopped and the sun came out. Noah sent a dove to find dry land. The dove came back with a leafy twig. "Hurrah!" shouted Noah. "The flood has ended." But many more days passed before the ark came to rest on dry land. Then Noah and all the animals came safely out of the ark, and life began again on the earth.

DUDLEY
AND THE
STRAWBERRY SHAKE

PETER CROSS
Text by JUDY TAYLOR

There was a soft breeze blowing in Shadyhanger and it carried the scent of strawberries through the open window.

Dudley had been awake since early morning searching for his special gloves. Today he was going strawberry picking.

The sun was shining strongly and the ground felt warm.

Dudley set off with his berry-barrow down the lane to the strawberry patch, and long before he got there his mouth was watering.

As he turned the corner, there they were before him – row upon row of fat, juicy strawberries.

Dudley picked a big strawberry very carefully with his special gloves.

He took a bite to see if it was ripe. It was.

He took another bite just to make sure … and another and another …

until there was nothing left.

Dudley was quite full up.

Just then, over by the hedge, Dudley spied an extra large strawberry, the largest he had ever seen.

"That's the one I'll take home for lunch," he said.

Dudley gripped the strawberry firmly with his gloves but it wouldn't come.

He tried again, pulling and pulling with all his might.

Suddenly the strawberry
began to shake
violently.

Dudley hung
on until he felt
his hands slipping
out of his gloves.

Then he was sailing
through the air. He landed
on the grass with a BUMP.

"What an odd
strawberry," thought
Dudley, feeling
rather giddy.

Dudley waited until the world
had stopped going round.

"It feels like time for a nap," he
said, hurrying home.

And just as he
was drifting off
to sleep,
Dudley
remembered
he had left
his gloves
behind.

Oh, Little Jack

by Inga Moore

It was a windy day. Little Jack Rabbit went into the garden. Mummy was in her vegetable patch. She was pulling out onions. "Can I help?" asked Little Jack. Little Jack Rabbit found an onion with a brown curly top. He tugged and he tugged. He tugged as hard as he could. But he couldn't pull it out of the ground.

"Oh, Little Jack!" said Mummy. "I think you are too small to pull out onions."

In the garden the wind was blowing down the leaves. "I shall have to sweep up these leaves," said Daddy.

"Can I do it?" asked Little Jack. Little Jack Rabbit ran to fetch the broom. But the broom was very long. He couldn't make it sweep. "Oh, Little Jack!" said Daddy. "I think you are too small to sweep up leaves."

Little Jack Rabbit went to Heathery Heath with his sister Nancy and his big brother Buck. Buck flew his new blue kite.

"Can I fly it?" asked Little Jack.
Little Jack Rabbit held the kite
by its string. He held it as tightly
as he could. But the wind pulled
and pulled. It nearly pulled
the kite away.

"Oh, Little Jack!" said Buck.
"I think you are too small to
fly a kite."
On the way home Nancy rode
her billy-cart down the hill.
"Can I have a turn?" asked Little
Jack.
Little Jack Rabbit sat in the
billy-cart.
He rode
it down
the hill.
But he couldn't
make it stop
at the
bottom.

"Oh, Little
Jack!" said
Nancy.
"I think you
are too small
to ride in a
billy-cart."

At home, Little Jack Rabbit went into the kitchen. His sisters Rhona and Rita were helping Mummy to make the tea. She was going to take some to Granpa.

"Can I take it?" asked Little Jack. Little Jack Rabbit picked up the cup. He carried it as carefully as he could. But he spilt the tea into the saucer.

"Oh, Little Jack!" said Rita. "I think you are too small to carry a cup of tea."

Poor Little Jack Rabbit ran to find his granpa.

"What's the matter, Little Jack?" Granpa asked.

"I am too small," said Little Jack.

"Too small for what?" asked Granpa.

"I am too small for everything," said Little Jack.

Granpa had been busy in his workshop.

He had been fixing something. It was a little red tricycle.

"Who is it for?" asked Little Jack.

"It can't be for me," said Mummy. "I am too big. And it can't be for Daddy. He's much too big."

"Is it for Buck?" asked Little Jack. No, the tricycle was not for Buck. It was not for Nancy or Rhona or Rita. They were all too big to ride it.

"Can I ride it?" asked Little Jack.

It was better than flying a kite. It was even better than riding in a billy-cart. And it was much better than carrying a cup of tea. "Thank you, Granpa," said Little Jack.

That night Little Jack Rabbit sat by the fire with his family. Now he was glad he was small. And not only because of the little red tricycle. There was something else, something he had forgotten. He was just the right size to sit on Granpa's knee.

Little Jack Rabbit climbed on to the little red tricycle. He was not too big and he was not too small. "Why, Little Jack!" said Granpa. "You are just the right size. The tricycle must be for you."

Little Jack Rabbit rode his little red tricycle round and round the garden. It was better than pulling up onions or sweeping leaves.

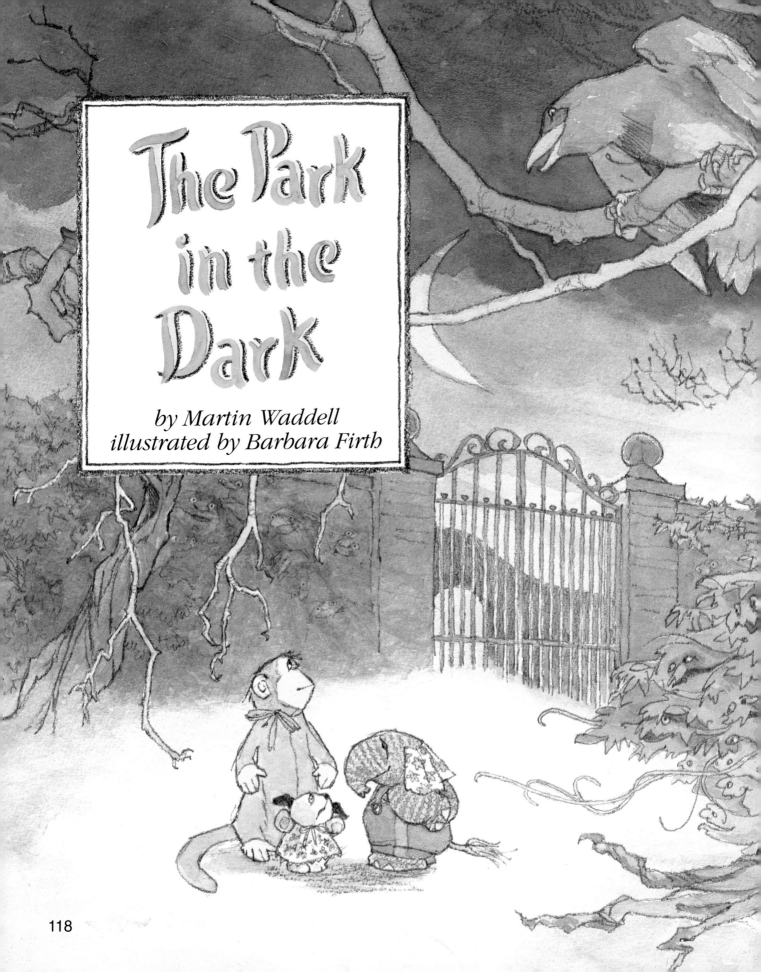

The Park in the Dark

by Martin Waddell
illustrated by Barbara Firth

When the sun goes down
and the moon comes up
and the old swing creaks in the dark,
that's when we go to the park,
  me and Loopy and Little Gee,
  all three.

Softly down the staircase,
through the haunty hall,
trying to look small,
  me and Loopy and Little Gee,
  we three.

It's shivery out in the dark
on our way to the park,
down dustbin alley,
past the ruined mill, so still,
  just me and Loopy and Little Gee,
  just three.

And Little Gee doesn't like it.
He's scared of the things he might see
in the park in the dark
with Loopy and me.
  That's me and Loopy and Little Gee,
  the three.

There might be moon witches
or man-eating trees
or withers that wobble
or old Scrawny Shins
or hairy hobgoblins,
or black boggarts' knees in the trees,
or things we can't see,
  me and Loopy and Little Gee,
  all three.

But there's not, says Loopy,
and I agree,
and Little Gee gets up on my back
and we pass the Howl Tree,
    me and Loopy and Little Gee.
        We're heroes, we three.

In the park in the dark
by the lake and the bridge,
that's when we see
where we want to be,
    me and Loopy
        and Little Gee.
            WHOOPEE!

And we swing and we slide
and we dance and we jump
and we chase all over the place,
me and Loopy
    and Little Gee,
        the Big Three!

And then the THING comes!
Y A A A A A
A A A I I I
O O O O O E E E E E E E !

RUN RUN RUN
shouts Little Gee to Loopy and me
and we flee,
    me and Loopy
        and Little Gee,
            scared three.

Back where we've come
through the park in the dark
and the THING is roaring
and following, see?
  After me and Loopy
  and Little Gee,
    we three.

Up to the
house, to the stair,
to the bed where we ought to be,
me and Loopy and Little Gee,
  safe as can be,
    all three.

FLY BY NIGHT

O nce, at the edge of a wood,
lived two owls, a mother owl
and her young one, Blink. Every day,
all day long, they slept. Every night,
all night long, the mother owl flew
and Blink waited.

One day, when the sun was still low in
the sky, Blink opened one eye and said,
"Now? Is it time?"

"Soon," said his mother. "Soon.
Go back to sleep."

Blink tried to sleep. When
the sun rose and warmed
the earth, he opened the
other eye. "*Now* is it time?"
"Not yet," said his mother.
"Soon. Go back to sleep."
Blink tried.

Butterflies looped and drifted
past him. Beetles scuttled
in the undergrowth.
Near by, a woodpecker
tapped on a tree trunk.
Blink couldn't sit still.
"Is it time *yet*?" he said.
His mother opened her
eyes. "You are old enough
and strong enough –"
Blink dithered with
excitement – "but you must
wait." His mother closed
her eyes.

The sun was at its highest.
A squirrel leapt from tree to
tree, quicker than a thought.
Along Blink's branch it came,
right past him, its tail
streaming out behind.
Blink wriggled and jiggled.
He *couldn't* sit still. All that
long afternoon, he watched
and waited. He shuffled and
fidgeted. Below, in the
clearing, a deer and its fawn
browsed on leaves and twigs.
High above, a kestrel
hovered, dipped and soared
again into the sky.
"When will it be *my* time?"
said Blink to himself.
Towards dusk, a sudden gust
of wind, sweeping through
the wood, lifting leaves on

their branches, seemed to gather
Blink from his branch as if it
would lift him too. "Time to fly,"
it seemed to say. Blink fluffed out
his feathers. He shifted his wings.
But the wind swirled by.
It was all puff and nonsense.

Blink sighed.

He closed his eyes.

123

The sun slipped behind the
fields. The moon rose pale and
clear. A night breeze stirred.

"Time to fly."

"Puff and nonsense,"
muttered Blink.

"*Time to fly,*" said his
mother beside him.

Blink sat up. "Is it?" he said.
"Is it? *Really?*"

The grey dusk had deepened.
Blink heard soft whisperings.
He saw the stars in the sky.
He felt the dampness of the
night air. He knew it was time to fly.
He gathered his strength. He drew
himself up. He stretched out his wings
and – lifted into the air.

Higher and higher. He flew. Further and further. Over the wood, over the fields, over the road and the sleeping city. High in the sky, his wing-beats strong,

Blink flew on over the sleeping city – and over the fields and the winding river. His first flight; a fly-by-night.

In the Rain
with
Baby Duck

*P*_{it-pat.}
Pit-a-pat.
Pit-a-pit-a-pat.

Oh, the rain came down. It poured and poured. Baby Duck was cross. She did not like walking in the rain. But it was Pancake Sunday, a Duck family tradition, and Baby loved pancakes.

And she loved Grandpa, who was waiting on the other side of town.

Pit-pat. Pit-a-pat. Pit-a-pit-a-pat.

"Follow us! Step lively!" Mr and Mrs Duck left the house arm in arm.

"Wet feet," wailed Baby.

"Don't dally, dear. Don't drag behind," called Mr Duck.

by Amy Hest
illustrated by Jill Barton

"Wet face," pouted Baby. "Water in my eyes."

Mrs Duck pranced along. "See how the rain rolls off your back!"

"Mud," muttered Baby. "Mud, mud, mud."

"Don't dawdle, dear! Don't lag behind!"

Mr and Mrs Duck skipped ahead. They waddled. They shimmied. They hopped in all the puddles. Baby dawdled. She dallied and pouted and dragged behind.

She sang a little song.

"I do not like the rain one bit
Splashing down my neck.
Baby feathers soaking wet,
I do not like this mean old day."

"Are you singing?" called Mr and Mrs Duck. "What a fine thing to do in the rain!"

Baby stopped singing.

Grandpa was waiting at the front door. He put his arm round Baby.

"Wet feet?" he asked.

"Yes," Baby said.

"Wet face?" Grandpa asked.

"Yes," Baby said.

"Mud?" Grandpa asked.

"Yes," Baby said. "Mud, mud, mud."

"I'm afraid the rain makes Baby cranky," clucked Mr Duck.

"I've never heard of a duck who doesn't like rain," worried Mrs Duck.

"Oh, really?" Grandpa kissed Baby's cheeks.

Grandpa took Baby's hand.

"Come with me, Baby."

They went upstairs to the attic.

"We are looking for a tall, green bag," Grandpa said.

Finally they found it. Inside was a beautiful red umbrella. There were matching boots, too.

"These used to be your mother's," Grandpa whispered. "A long time ago, she was a baby duck who did not like rain."

Baby opened the umbrella. The boots were just the right size.

Baby and Grandpa marched downstairs.

"My boots!" cried Mrs Duck. "And my bunny umbrella!"

"No, mine!" said Baby.

"You look lovely," said Mrs Duck.

Mr Duck put a plate of pancakes on the table. After that, Baby and Grandpa went outside.

Pit-pat. Pit-a-pat. Pit-a-pit-a-pat.

Oh, the rain came down. It poured and poured. Baby Duck and Grandpa walked arm in arm in the rain.

They waddled.

They shimmied.

They hopped in all the puddles.

And Baby Duck sang a new song.

"I really like the rain a lot
*   Splashing my umbrella.*
Big red boots on baby feet,
*   I really love this rainy day."*

We're the noisy dinosaurs, *crash, bang, wallop!*
We're the noisy dinosaurs, *crash, bang, wallop!*
If you're sleeping, we'll wake you up!
We're the noisy dinosaurs, *crash, bang, wallop!*

We're the hungry dinosaurs, *um, um, um!*
We're the hungry dinosaurs, *um, um, um!*
We want eggs with jam on top!
We're the hungry dinosaurs, *um, um, um!*

We're the busy dinosaurs, *play, play, play!*
We're the busy dinosaurs, *play, play, play!*
We've got toys to share with you!
We're the busy dinosaurs, *play, play, play!*

We're the happy dinosaurs, *ha, ha, ha!*
We're the happy dinosaurs, *ha, ha, ha!*
We tell jokes and tickle each other!
We're the happy dinosaurs, *ha, ha, ha!*

We're the dancing dinosaurs, *quick, quick, slow!*
We're the dancing dinosaurs,
quick, quick, slow!
Hold our hands but don't step
on our feet!
We're the dancing dinosaurs,
quick, quick, slow!

DINOSAURS! BY JOHN WATSON

We're the thirsty dinosaurs, *slurp, slurp, glug!*
We're the thirsty dinosaurs, *slurp, slurp, glug!*
We'll drink the sea and your bathwater too!
We're the thirsty dinosaurs, *slurp, slurp, glug!*

CRASH!

We're the angry dinosaurs, *roar, roar, roar!*
We're the angry dinosaurs, *roar, roar, roar!*
Get out of our way or we'll eat you up!
We're the angry dinosaurs, *roar, roar, roar!*

We're the naughty dinosaurs, *bad, bad, bad!*
We're the naughty dinosaurs, *bad, bad, bad!*
We say sorry and promise to be good!
We're the naughty dinosaurs, *bad, bad, bad!*

We're the quiet dinosaurs, *shh, shh, shh!*
We're the quiet dinosaurs, *shh, shh, shh!*
We read books and play hide-and-seek!
We're the quiet dinosaurs, *shh, shh, shh!*

We're the dirty dinosaurs, *scrub, scrub, scrub!*
We're the dirty dinosaurs, *scrub, scrub, scrub!*
We wash our necks and brush our teeth!
We're the dirty dinosaurs, *scrub, scrub, scrub!*

We're the sleepy dinosaurs, *yawn, yawn, yawn!*
We're the sleepy dinosaurs, *yawn, yawn, yawn!*
Send us to bed with a great big kiss!
We're the sleepy dinosaurs,
yawn, yawn, yawn!

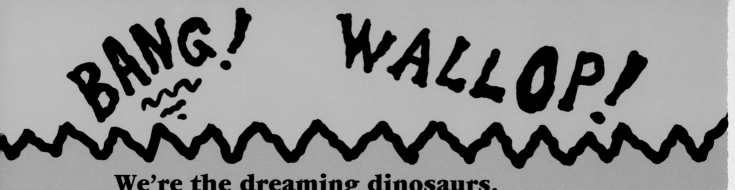

BANG! WALLOP!

We're the dreaming dinosaurs,
snore, snore, snore!
We're the dreaming dinosaurs,
snore,
snore,
snore!

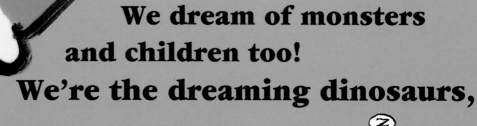

We dream of monsters
and children too!
We're the dreaming dinosaurs,
snore, snore,
snore!

The Three Billy Goats Gruff

illustrated by

Charlotte Voake

Once upon a time three billy-goats lived together in a field on a hillside. Their names were Big Billy-goat Gruff, Middle Billy-goat Gruff, and Little Billy-goat Gruff.

A river ran beside the billy-goats' field, and one day they decided to cross it, to eat the grass on the other side. But first they had to go over the bridge, and under the bridge lived a great ugly Troll.

First Little Billy-goat Gruff stepped on to the bridge.

TRIP TRAP, TRIP TRAP, went his hoofs.

"Who's that tripping over my bridge?" roared the Troll.

"It is only I, Little Billy-goat Gruff, going across the river to make myself fat," said Little Billy-goat Gruff, in such a small voice.

"Now I'm coming to gobble you up," said the Troll.

"Oh please don't eat me, I'm so small," said Little Billy-goat Gruff. "Wait for the next billy-goat, he's much bigger."

"Well, be off with you," said the Troll.

A little while later, Middle Billy-goat Gruff stepped on to the bridge. TRIP TRAP, TRIP TRAP, went his hoofs.

"Who's that tripping over my bridge?" roared the Troll.

"It is only I, Middle Billy-goat Gruff, going across the river to make myself fat," said Middle Billy-goat Gruff, whose voice was not so small.

"Now I'm coming to gobble you up," said the Troll.

"Oh no, don't eat me," said Middle Billy-goat Gruff. "Wait for the next billy-goat, he's the biggest of all."

"Very well, be off with you," said the Troll.

It wasn't long before Big Billy-goat Gruff stepped on to the bridge.

TRIP TRAP, TRIP TRAP, TRIP TRAP, went his hoofs, and the bridge groaned under his weight.

"Who's that tramping over my bridge?" roared the Troll.

"It is I, Big Billy-goat Gruff," said Big Billy-goat Gruff, who had a rough, roaring voice of his own.

"Now I'm coming to gobble you up," said the Troll, and at once he jumped on to the bridge, immensely horrible and hungry.

But Big Billy-goat Gruff was very fierce and strong. He put down his head and charged the Troll and butted him so hard he flew high into the air and then fell down, down, down, *splash* into the middle of the river. And the great ugly Troll was never seen again.

Then Big Billy-goat Gruff joined Middle Billy-goat Gruff and Little Billy-goat Gruff in the field on the far side of the river. There they got so fat that they could hardly walk home again, and if the fat hasn't fallen off them, they're still fat now.

So *snip, snap, snout,* this tale's told out!

John Joe and the Big Hen

by Martin Waddell   illustrated by Paul Howard

"It's your day for minding John Joe," Mammy told Sammy, so he had to stay with John Joe. Mary read her book and Mammy went on with her work. Splinter the dog sat in the sun and got toasted.

Sammy got bored minding John Joe. Sammy wanted to play with his friend, Willie Brennan. "I'm away down Cow Lane to the Brennans'," Sammy told Mary.

"Take John Joe with you," said Mary, but Sammy took Splinter instead of John Joe.

"I'm left by myself!" John Joe told Mary. "You'd better tell Mammy!"

"Let Mammy get on with her work," Mary said. "I'll settle our Sammy!"

Mary took John Joe by the hand and set off down Cow Lane to find Sammy.

They went to the Brennans', but there was no sign of Sammy! Mary was mad, for it wasn't her day for minding John Joe.

"Do you think they'd be down by the stream?" asked John Joe.

"I'd look, but you are too little to go," Mary said. "And I can't leave you here with no one to mind you."

"I'll mind myself!" said John Joe.

The Brennans' big hen came to look at John Joe. John Joe was used to the hens at his house, but he didn't know the Brennans' big hen.

John Joe climbed on the wall, for he thought that the Brennans' big hen might eat him.

"MRS BRENNAN!" shouted John Joe, but Mrs Brennan was out.

"MARY!" yelled John Joe, but Mary had gone after Sammy and she couldn't hear him.

"OH MAMMY!" wailed John Joe, but Mammy was safe back at home.

That left John Joe alone with the Brennans' big hen and so … John Joe ran away from the hen!

"I'm not scared of you!" John Joe told the hen.

"I'll whack your backside," John Joe told the hen.

"Go away home, hen!" John Joe told the hen … but the big hen didn't go.

Mary came back to the Brennans' with Sammy and Splinter, but…

"Where's our John Joe?" Sammy said.

"JOHN JOE! JOHN JOE! OUR JOHN JOE!" shouted Sammy.

"JOHN JOE!" shouted Mary.

No John Joe with the hens in the yard.
No John Joe with the pigs in the sty.

No John Joe in the ditch.
No John Joe in the barn.

"Go find John Joe, Splinter!" said Sammy.

Splinter walked round and sniffed at the ground … and the wall … and the top of the wall.

Then Splinter dived into the corn.

Splinter barked and he barked and he barked…

138

WOOF! WOOF! WOOF!

John Joe was asleep in the corn.

"The big hen chased me!" said John Joe.

"We thought you were lost," said Mary, as she carried John Joe up the lane.

"John Joe was scared by the Brennans' big hen," Mary told Mammy. "He hid away in the corn. We thought that we'd lost our little John Joe."

"There's no way I'm losing my little John Joe!" Mammy said.

"It was your day for minding John Joe," Mary told Sammy.

"Sure, I minded myself," said John Joe.

Contrary Mary

by Anita Jeram

 When Mary got up this morning she was feeling contrary. She put her cap on back to front and her shoes on the wrong feet.

"Are you awake, Mary?" her mum called.

"No!" said Contrary Mary.

For breakfast there was hot toast with peanut butter.

"What would you like, Mary?" asked Mum.

"Roast potatoes and gravy, please," said Contrary Mary.

When they went to the shops it was raining.

"Come under the umbrella, Mary," said Mum.

 But Contrary Mary didn't. She just danced about, getting wet.

All day long, Contrary Mary did contrary things.

She rode her bicycle, backwards. She went for a walk, on her hands. She read a book upside down.

She flew her kite along the ground.

Mary's mum shook her head.

"Mary, Mary, quite contrary," she said.

And then she had an idea.

That evening, at bedtime, instead of tucking Mary in the right way round, Mary's mum tucked her in upside down.

Then she opened the curtains, turned on the light, kissed Mary's toes and said, "Good morning!"

Mary laughed and laughed.

"Contrary Mum!" she said.

"Do you love me, Contrary Mary?" asked Mary's mum, giving her a cuddle.

"No!" said Contrary Mary. And she gave her mum a great big kiss.

CUDDLY DUDLEY

Dudley loved to play. He loved to play jumping, diving and splashing. But most of all Dudley loved to play … all by himself.

The trouble was, Dudley was such a lovely cuddly penguin that whenever his brothers and sisters found him on his own they just couldn't resist having a huddle and a waddle and a cuddle with him.

"Go away," Dudley would say. "Leave me alone."

"We can't," came the reply. "You're just too cuddly, Dudley."

"I'm fed up with all your huddling and waddling and cuddling," said Dudley one day. "I'm going to find a place where I can play all on my own."

And off he went.

He waddled and he toddled for many, many miles until, quite by chance, he found a little wooden house which looked perfect for a penguin.

And it seemed to be empty.

"At last!" said Dudley. "A house of my own – a place where I can jump about all day without being disturbed."

Just then there came a rap-tap-tap at the little wooden door.

"It's us," said two of Dudley's sisters. "We followed your waddleprints. Can we come in?"

"No, you jolly well can't," said Dudley. "I'm very busy and I don't want to be disturbed, so please go away." And he shut the little wooden door and was alone once more.

"At last!" said Dudley. "A house of my own – a place where I can splash about all day without being…"

Just then there came a rap-tap-tap at the little wooden door.

"It's us," said his brothers and sisters. "We followed your waddleprints. Can we come in and…?"

"No, you jolly well can't," said Dudley. "I don't want

BY JEZ ALBOROUGH

to huddle and waddle and cuddle. So for the very last time ... STOP FOLLOWING ME AROUND!"

He slammed the little wooden door and was alone once more.

"At last!" sighed Dudley. "A house of my own..."

BANG, BANG, BANG went the little wooden door.

"That does it," he said. "When I catch those penguins I'll..."

But it wasn't the penguins at the little wooden door. It was a great big man.

"My word!" said the great big man. "What an adorable penguin! *Give us a cuddle!*" he cried, and chased Dudley all round the house and out into the snow.

Dudley ran and ran and escaped from the man. Then he decided to head back home. But which way was home?

Crunch, crunch, crunch went Dudley, looking for some waddleprints to follow. But when night came, he was still alone ... and completely lost ... and now, for the first time, he was lonely. He climbed a hill to get a better view, and at the top

he saw an enormous orange moon with hundreds of tiny sparkling stars huddled all around.

"Excuse me," said a penguin from the foot of the hill. "Have you finished being alone yet? Only we wondered, now that you're back ... if you wouldn't mind ... whether we could ... it's just that you're so ... *so*..."

"CUDDLY!" shouted Dudley. And he bounced down the hill as fast as he could.

Then Dudley and all his brothers and sisters had the best huddling, waddling, cuddling session that they'd *ever* had. UNTIL ...

"GIVE US A CUDDLE!"

143

Quacky quack-quack!

by **Ian Whybrow**   illustrated by **Russell Ayto**

This little baby had some bread;
His mummy gave it to him
  for the ducks,
But he started eating it instead.

Lots of little ducky things
  came swimming along,
Thinking it was feeding time,
  but they were wrong!

The baby held on to the bag,
  he wouldn't let go;
And the crowd of noisy ducky birds
  started to grow.

They made a lot of ducky noises …
  quacky quack-quack!
Then a whole load of geese swam up
  and went *honk! honk!* at the back.

And when a band went marching by,
  in gold and red and black,
Nobody could hear the tune –
  all they could hear was …
  honk! honk! quacky quack-quack!

honk! honk!

quacky quack-quack!

toot! toot!

"Louder, boys," said the bandmaster,
  "give it a bit more puff."
So the band went _toot! toot!_
  ever so loud,
But it still wasn't enough.

Then all over the city,
  including the city zoo,
All the animals heard the noise and
  started making noises too.

All the donkeys went _ee-aw! ee-aw!_
All the dogs went _woof! woof!_
All the snakes went _sss-ssss!_
All the crocodiles went _snap! snap!_
All the mice went _squeaky-squeaky!_
All the lions went …

roar!

_ee-aw! ee-aw!_

woof! woof!

sss-ssss!

snap! snap!

squeaky - squeaky!

Then one little boy piped up and said,
"I know what this is all about.
That's my baby brother with the
    bag of bread;
I'll soon have this sorted out."

He ran over to where the baby
    was holding his bag of bread
And not giving any to the birdies,
    but eating it instead.

And he said, "What about some
    for the ducky birds?"
But the baby started to …

scream!

So his brother said, "If you let me
    hold the bag,
I'll let you hold my ice-cream."

Then the boy said, "Quiet all
    you quack-quacks!
And stop pushing, you're all
    going to get fed."
And he put his hand in the paper bag
    and brought out a handful of bread.

So all the birds went quiet
    and the band stopped playing too…
And all the animals stopped
    making a noise,
Including the animals in the zoo.

And suddenly the baby realized
    they were all waiting for a crumb!
So he gave the ice-cream back
    and he took a great big handful
        of bread and …
Threw all the ducky birds some.

Then all the hungry ducky birds
were ever so glad they'd come,
And instead of going ...
honk! honk! quacky quack-quack!
All the birdies said ...

YUM! YUM!

Marlon sat on the floor watching TV. Marlon's granny sat in the armchair, watching Marlon.

"He's getting too old for that dummy," she said sternly to Marlon's mum.

"It's a noo-noo," said Marlon.

"He calls it a noo-noo," explained Marlon's mum.

"Well, what*ever* he calls it," said Marlon's granny, "he looks like an idiot with that stupid great *thing* stuck in his mouth all the time."

"He doesn't have it *all* the time," soothed Marlon's mum. "Only at night or if he's a bit tired. He's a bit tired now – aren't you, pet?"

"Mmmmm," said Marlon.

"His teeth will start sticking out," warned Marlon's granny.

"Monsters' teeth stick out anyway," observed Marlon.

"Don't answer back," said Marlon's granny. "You should just throw them *all* away," she continued. "At this rate he'll be starting *school* with a dummy. At this

rate he'll be starting *work* with a dummy. You'll just have to be firm with him."

"Well," said Marlon's mum, "I am *thinking* about it. We'll start next week, won't we Marlon? Now you're a big boy, we'll just get rid of all those silly noo-noos, won't we?"

"No," said Marlon.

"You see!" said Marlon's granny. "One word from you and he does as he likes."

There was no doubt about it. Marlon was a hopeless case.

Marlon's mum decided to take drastic action. She gathered up every single noo-noo she could find and dumped them all in the dustbin five minutes before the rubbish truck arrived. But Marlon had made plans just in case the worst should happen. He had secret noo-noo supplies all over the house.

NOO-NOO

by Jill Murphy

There was a yellow one down the side of the armchair, a blue one at the back of the breadbin, various different types in his toy ambulance and his favourite pink one was lurking in the toe of his wellington boot.

His mother and granny were astonished. They could not think where he kept finding them.

"You'll be teased when you go out to play," warned his granny. "A great big monster like you with a baby's dummy."

Marlon knew about this already. The other monsters had been teasing him for ages, but he loved his noo-noos so much that he didn't care.

The other monsters often lay in wait and jumped out on Marlon as he passed by with his noo-noo twirling.

"Who's a big baby, then?" jeered Basher.

"Does the little baby need his dummy, then?" sneered Alligatina.

"Who's his mummy's little darling?" cooed Boomps-a-daisy.

Marlon always ignored their taunts.

"You're just jealous," he replied.

"You all wish you'd got one too."

Gradually, the secret supply of noo-noos dwindled. Marlon's mum refused to buy any more and they all began to be lost, or thrown away by Marlon's mum. Finally, there was only one left, the pink one. Marlon kept it with him all the time. Either in his mouth or under his pillow or in the toe of his wellington boot, where no one thought to look.

To his delight, Marlon found one extra noo-noo that his mum had missed. It was a blue one, which had fallen down the side of his bed and been covered up by a sock. He knew his best pink noo-noo wouldn't last for ever, so he crept out and planted the blue one in the garden.

All the other monsters decided to gang up on Marlon. They collected lots of different bits of junk and fixed them all together until they had made just what they wanted. It was a noo-noo snatcher.

Then they waited behind a bush until Marlon came past with his pink noo-noo twirling.

"Here he comes," said Alligatina.

"Grab it!" yelled Boomps-a-daisy.

"Now!" said Basher.

With one quick hooking movement, they caught the ring of the noo-noo with the noo-noo snatcher and pulled!

But Marlon clenched his teeth and held on. Monsters have the most powerful jaws in the world. Once they have decided to hang on, that's *it*. Marlon hung on, the monsters hung on to the noo-noo snatcher and there they stayed, both sides pulling with all their monster might.

And there they would *still* be, if Marlon had not decided, just at that very moment, that perhaps he was too old to have a noo-noo any more.

So, he let go. And all the other monsters went whizzing off down the road, across the park and into the pond with a mighty splash.

Marlon went home. "I've given up my noo-noo," he said. "I sort of threw it into the pond."

"Good gracious me!" exclaimed Marlon's mum, sitting down suddenly with the shock.

"I told you," said Marlon's granny. "You just have to be firm."

"Actually," said Marlon, "I've planted one, so I'll have a noo-noo tree – just in case I change my mind."

"That's nice, dear," said Marlon's mum.

"Nonsense!" said Marlon's granny. "Dummies don't grow on trees. A noo-noo tree! How ridiculous!"

Two Shoes, New Shoes

Two shoes, new shoes,
 Bright shiny blue shoes.

High-heeled ladies' shoes
 For standing tall,
Button-up baby's shoes,
 Soft and small.

Slippers, warm by the fire,
 Lace-ups in the street.
Gloves are for hands
 And socks are for feet.

A crown made of paper,
 A hat with a feather,
Sun hats, fun hats,
 Hats for bad weather.

by Shirley Hughes

A clean white T-shirt
  Laid on the bed,
Two holes for arms
  And one for the head.

Zip up a zipper,
  Button a coat,
A shoe for a bed,
  A hat for a boat.

Wearing it short
  And wearing it long,
Getting it right
  And getting it wrong.

Trailing finery,
  Dressed for a ball
And into the bath
  Wearing nothing at all!

THIS IS THE BEAR

— AND THE —

BAD LITTLE GIRL

by Sarah Hayes   *illustrated by Helen Craig*

This is the bear who went out to eat.
This is the dog who stayed in the street.

This is the girl with the curly hair
who said she really liked the bear.

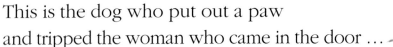

This is the dog who put out a paw
and tripped the woman who came in the door …

which pushed the people waiting to pay
and made the waiter drop the tray.

This is the boy all covered in cream
who went to the kitchen to wash his face clean.

This is the girl with the curly hair
who said, "You're coming with me, bear."

This is the girl who walked down the street
holding the bear by one of his feet.

This is the dog who thought it was fun
when the bad little girl began to run.

This is the girl who ran faster and faster
but this is the dog who ran right past her.

This is the girl
who gave the bear back
and said he was
only a baggy old sack.
This is the boy
who said, "I don't care
if he's saggy or baggy,
he's still *my* bear."

My Mum and Dad Make Me Laugh

My mum and dad make me laugh. One likes spots and the other likes stripes.

My mum likes spots in winter and spots in summer. My dad likes stripes on weekdays and stripes at weekends.

by Nick Sharratt

Last weekend we went to the safari park. My mum put on her spottiest dress and earrings, and my dad put on his stripiest suit and tie.
I put on my grey top and trousers.
"You do like funny clothes!" said my mum and dad.

We set off in the car and on the way we stopped for something to eat.
My mum had a spotty pizza and my dad had a stripy ice-cream.
I had a bun.
"You do like funny food!" said my mum and dad.

When we got to the safari park it was very exciting.
My mum liked the big cats best.
"Those are splendid spots," she said. "And I should know!"
My dad liked the zebras best.
"Those are super stripes," he said. "And I should know!"

But the animals I liked best didn't have spots and didn't have stripes.
They were big and grey and eating their tea.
"Those are really good elephants," I said.

"And I should know!"

WHERE'S MY MUM?

by Leon Rosselson

illustrated by Priscilla Lamont

Where's my mum?
She's not in the drawer,
Or under the bed,
Or behind the door.

She's not in the bath,
Unless she's got
Turned into
    a spider.
I hope she's not!

I'll look in the mirror;
Who can that be
With the scowly face?
It must be me!

She's not in the fridge
With the strawberry jelly,
The chicken, the milk and
The something smelly.

She's not in the cupboard.
What's that noise?
No, she's not
    in the box
With all my
    toys.

She's not
    in the piano
Or under the chair,
Or behind the curtains
Or anywhere.

I'll try the garden.
Where can she be?
She's not in the sky
Or the apple tree.

Look at those ants
    racing to
        and fro!
Have you seen
    my mum?
I think that
    means no.

Paint me a picture.
Play games
   with me.
Mum! I'm hungry.
I want my tea.

I can't see a mum
In the garden shed,
And she isn't a flower
In the flowerbed!

Mum! I can hop!
I can jump on the bed!
I can curl in a ball,
I can stand on my head.

Can I drink my milk in
My dinosaur mug?
Get up, Mum…
   And I'll give you a hug!

Perhaps she's in *her* bed.
I'll go and explore.
Back into the house;
Push open her door.

There's a lumpy shape –
I'll take a peep…
There's my mum,
And she's fast asleep!

Mum! Mum!
You should be awake.
Tell me a story!
Bake me a cake!

The Fat King

Once upon a time there was a fat king.

He lived in a fat house with his fat wife

 and fat children. He had a fat dog

and a fat cat. And fat birds sat in fat trees

under a fat sun. Everything in the garden was fat.

One day the king came downstairs and said hello to his kingdom. "Hello, dog and cat," he said.

"Hello, cabbages. Hello, potatoes. Hello, trees. Hello, world."

But when he came to the green oak tree he stopped and stared.

"Come and see this," he called to his wife and children. For there, under the tree, sitting in its shade, was a THIN bird.

"Shoo!" said the king and clapped his hands. "Shoo, little thin bird!" he said very loudly indeed.

But the little thin bird did not move. So the king gave him a dish of breadcrumbs and went off to consult the gardener.

"You could try chasing him," said William.

But the king said, "That will only frighten him. I will go and ask Fido instead."

And on the way to Fido he passed the green oak tree, and put down another dish of crumbs for the little thin bird.

"Hello, Fido," said the king. "I have called about the little thin bird."

by Graham Jeffery

Fido said, "I will come and bark at him." But the king said, "No, I do not want to startle him, I will go and see Tibby instead."

And as he passed the green oak tree he left a dish of milk for the little thin bird.

Tibby said, "I could jump over him and scratch him."

But the king said, "No, that will not do at all. I will go and ask the family. They will think of something kinder."

But his family did not know what to do. And the fisherman didn't know. And the vicar didn't know. And the postman didn't know.

And every time the king passed the green oak tree, he left a bowl of crumbs for the little thin bird.

The fat king said to his friends, "It is no good. It is no good at all. Nobody knows what to do about the little thin bird."

But then Fido looked under the green oak tree, and Tibby looked, and the king looked, and everybody looked.

And there under the green oak tree was … the fattest, plumpest bird you ever saw. And he hopped up into the green oak tree and went to sleep under the fat sun.

MOUSE PARTY

Mouse found a deserted house and decided to make his home there.

But it was a very big house for such a small mouse and he felt a little lonely.

"I know," he thought, "I'll have a party." So he sent invitations to all his friends.

The first to arrive were…

Cat with a **mat**  and **Dog** with a **log.**

Then came **Hare** with a **chair,**  **Owl** with a **towel,**

Giraffe with a **bath,**  **Hen** with a **pen,**

Lamb with some **jam,** 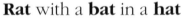 **Rat** with a **bat** in a **hat**

 and **Fox** with a **box** full of **lots** and **lots** of different kinds and colours of **socks.**

"Let's party!" said Mouse. But…

Rat-a-tat-tat!

It was an elephant with two trunks. He was

blowing through one and carrying the other.

"Hello," said Mouse. "Welcome to my house."

"*Your* house?" said the elephant and he looked rather cross.

"I've just been away on a long holiday.

This house, I must tell you, is mine!"

164

by **Alan Durant**
illustrated by **Sue Heap**

"Oh," said Mouse, Lamb, Hare, Rat and Bat.

"Oh," said Hen, Dog, Owl, Fox and Giraffe.

But, "Come in, come in!" said Cat. "You're just in time for the party."

"A party … for me?" said Elephant. "Oh my! Yippee!"

So they drank and they ate and they danced until late and had the most marvellous party. And later, when the guests had all gone home, leaving Elephant and Mouse alone,

Elephant said, "I think, little Mouse, perhaps it's true, there's room for us both in this house, don't you?"

165

The **Red Woollen Blanket**

by Bob Graham

Julia had her own blanket right from the start. Julia was born in the winter. She slept in her special cot wrapped tight as a parcel. She had a band of plastic on her wrist with her name on it.

"She's as bald as an egg," said her father, helping himself to another chocolate.

Julia came home from the hospital with her new red blanket, a bear, a grey woollen dog and a plastic duck.

Waiting at home for her were a large pair of pants with pink flowers and a beautiful blue jacket specially knitted by her grandmother.

"Isn't blue for boys?" said Dad.

"No, it doesn't really matter," said Mum.

Wrapped up in the red woollen blanket, Julia slept in her own basket or in the front garden in the watery winter sunshine. Her hair sprouted from the holes in her tea-cosy hat. She smiled – nothing worried Julia.

Julia grew. She slept in a cot and sucked and chewed the corners of her not-so-new blanket. She rubbed the red woollen blanket gently against her nose.

Julia's mum carried her to the shops in a pack on her back. The pack was meant to carry the shopping. Julia liked it so much up there that the pushchair was used for the shopping and the pack was used for Julia.

Then Julia was crawling and her blanket went with her. Some of it was left behind...

Then Julia took her first step.

Julia made her own small room from the blanket. It was pink twilight under there. From outside, the "creature" had a mind of its own.
It heaved and throbbed.

Wherever Julia went her blanket went too. In the spring, the summer, the autumn, and the winter.

Julia was getting bigger. Her blanket was getting smaller.

A sizeable piece was lost under the lawnmower.

"If Julia ran off deep into a forest," said her father, "she could find her way back by the blanket threads left behind."

The day that Julia started school, she had a handy little blanket not much bigger than a postage stamp – because it would never do to take a whole blanket to school … unless you were Billy, who used his blanket as a "Lone Avenger's" cape.

Sometime during Julia's first day at school, she lost the last threads of her blanket.

It may have been while playing in the school yard, or having her lunch under the trees. It could have been anywhere at all …

and she hardly missed it.

HANDA'S SURPRISE

Handa put seven delicious fruits in a basket
for her friend, Akeyo.
She will be surprised, thought Handa
as she set off for Akeyo's village.
I wonder which fruit she'll like best?

Will she like
the soft yellow banana …

or the sweet-
smelling guava?

Will she like the
round juicy orange …

or the ripe
red mango?

Will she like the
spiky-leaved pineapple …

the creamy
green avocado …

 or the tangy
purple passion-fruit?

Which fruit will Akeyo like best?

"Hello, Akeyo," said Handa. "I've brought you a surprise."
"Tangerines!" said Akeyo. "My favourite fruit."

"TANGERINES?" said Handa. "That *is* a surprise!"

SEBASTIAN'S TRUMPET

by Miko Imai

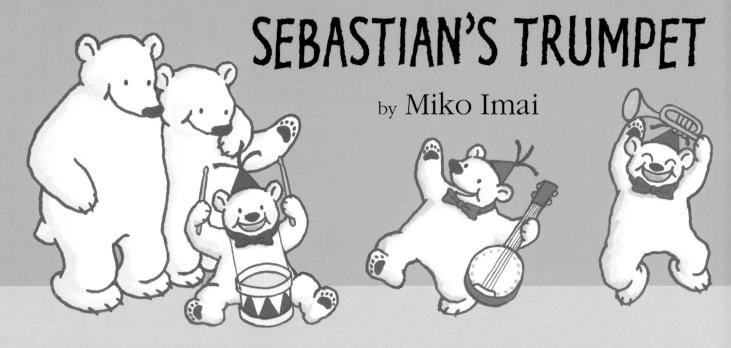

It was the three little bears' birthday. Daddy and Mummy Bear had some special presents for them. Theodore got a drum. Oswald got a banjo. And Sebastian got a trumpet.

"Let's play 'Happy Birthday!'" they shouted.
Theodore banged on his drum. Rat-a-tat-tat.
Oswald strummed his banjo. Twang Twang.
And Sebastian blew into his trumpet.
But the only sound it made was Pfffft.

"What's happened to your trumpet?" asked Theodore. "Let *me* try it … Pfffftt."
"Let *me* try!" said Oswald. "I bet I can do it … Pffffftt."

Theodore and Oswald played "Happy Birthday" for Daddy and Mummy Bear.

I wish I could play my trumpet,
thought Sebastian.

"Pffftt … I HATE this trumpet!"
Sebastian sobbed.

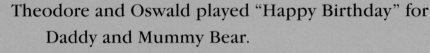

172

"Why did you give me a trumpet, Mummy?
It doesn't even work!"
"Maybe you're trying too hard," said Mummy
Bear. "Why don't you rest now and try
again later?"

When Sebastian woke up, he couldn't
wait to try his trumpet again.
He tiptoed towards it.

He picked it up and started to play.

Pffooott

Troooft

TA-TA-TA-
ROOOOOOON!
TA-TA-TA-
ROOOOOOON!

"You did it, Sebastian!" his brothers shouted.
And the three little bears all played
"Happy Birthday" together.

Twang
Twang

Rat-a-tat-tat

Toot
Toot

173

MONKEY TRICKS

 Horatio was practising hopping. HOP HOP HOP WHOOPS! He fell over a notice board. I'll ask James what this says, he thought.

James was looking in his Useful Box. Someone had untidied it. "What does this say?" asked Horatio.

"Johnny Conqueror Coming Today," said James. He looked worried. "That naughty monkey!" Horatio looked all around for Johnny Conqueror.

by Camilla Ashforth

"Jimmies and Jacks! Mind your backs!"
a voice called, and there was Johnny
Conqueror, pulling a wagon.

"I'm very good at juggling,"

           he boasted.

               He threw a string

                of beads into the

            air and held out his hands to catch them. But

he missed and the beads scattered everywhere.

Horatio clapped his hands.

      My beads look like this, thought

James, picking one up.

"For my next trick," shouted Johnny Conqueror, "I take a long piece of rope and knot it here and twist it a bit here…"

That rope looks useful, thought James.

He looked in his Useful Box again.

Johnny Conqueror got into a tangle. He needed James to untie him. Horatio thought it was very funny.

"I'll show you how clever I am at balancing," said Johnny Conqueror, jumping onto a cotton reel! He stood on one leg and spun a dish above him. The cotton reel wobbled.

James looked worried. If that was my dish … he thought.

CRASH! The cotton reel spun away. Johnny Conqueror fell over. The dish broke. Oh dear, thought James.

"Hooray!" shouted Horatio.

"To end the show," announced Johnny Conqueror, "I do my best trick. I disappear! All close your eyes and count to five."

"One … two …" Horatio began.

"I know who untidied my Useful Box," whispered James.

"Three … four …" added Horatio.

"And I'm going to catch him," James said.

"Five!" shouted Horatio and they opened their eyes. Johnny Conqueror had disappeared.

"Bother," said James. "He got away."

James began to tidy up.

"Now I can show you my trick," said Horatio, and he hopped for James. James clapped his hands.

"That really is clever," he said, and gave Horatio a big hug.

The Little Boat

by Kathy Henderson

illustrated by Patrick Benson

Down by the shore
where the sea meets the land,
licking at the pebbles
sucking at the sand,
and the wind flaps
the sunshades
and the ice-cream man
out-shouts the seagulls
and the people come
with buckets and spades
and suntan lotion
to play on the shore
by the edge of the ocean,

a little boy
made himself a boat
from an old piece of
polystyrene plastic,
with a stick for a mast
and a string tail sail
and he splashed
and he played
with the boat he'd made
digging it a harbour
scooping it a creek,
all day long by the edge
of the sea,
singing
*'We are unsinkable
my boat and me!'*

Until he turned his back
and a small wind blew
and the little boat drifted
away from the shore,
out of his reach
across the waves,
past the swimmers
and air beds,
away from the beach.

And the boat
sailed out
in the skim of the wind
past the fishermen
sitting on the end of the pier,

out and out
past a crab boat trailing
a row of floats
and a dinghy sailing
a zig-zag track
across the wind,

out where the lighthouse
beam beats by
where the sea birds wheel
in the sky and dive
for the silvery fish
just beneath the waves,
out sailed the little boat
out and away.

And it bobbed by
a tugboat chugging home
from leading a liner
out to sea
and it churned in the wake,
still further out,
of a giant tanker
as high as a house
and as long as a road,
on sailed the little boat
all alone.

And the further it sailed
the bigger grew
the ocean

until all around
was sea
and not a sign of land,
not a leaf,
not a bird,
not a sound,
just the wind
and heaving sliding
gliding breathing water
under endless sky.

179

And hours went by
and days went by
and still the little boat
sailed on,
with once a glimpse
of the lights from an oil rig
standing in the distance
on giant's legs
and sometimes
the shape of a ship
like a toy,
hanging in the air
at the rim of the world,

or a bit of driftwood
or rubbish passing,
otherwise nothing,
on and on.

And then came a day
when the sky went dark
and the seas grew uneasy
and tossed about
and the wind
that had whispered
began to roar
and the waves grew bigger
and lashed and tore
and hurled great manes
of spray
in the air
like flames in a fire

and all night long
as the seas grew rougher
the little boat danced
with the wind
and the weather

till the morning came
and the storm was over
and all was calm and still
and quiet again.

180

And then suddenly
up from underneath
with a thrust and a leap
and a mouth full of teeth
came a great fish snapping
for something to eat,
and it grabbed the boat
and dived

deep

deep

deep

down

to where the light grows dim
in the depths of the sea,
a world of fins and claws
and slippery things
and rocks and wrecks
of ancient ships
and ocean creatures
no one's seen

where,
finding that plastic
wasn't food,
the fish spat out
the boat again
and up it flew,
up up up up
like the flight of an arrow
towards the light,
burst through the silver skin
of the sea
and floated on
in the calm sunshine.

Then a small breeze came
and the small breeze grew,
steadily pushing
the boat along,
and now sea birds called
in the sky again
and a boat sailed near
and another
and then,
in the beat of the sun
and the silent air,
a sound could be heard,
waves breaking somewhere
and the sea swell curled
and the white surf rolled
the little boat on
and on
towards land.

And there at the shore
where the sea greets the land,
licking at the pebbles
sucking at the sand,
a child was standing,
she stretched out her hand
and picked up the boat
from the waves at her feet
and all day long
she splashed and she played
with the boat she'd found
at the edge of the sea,
singing
'We are unsinkable
my boat and me!'

"Not me," said the monkey

"Who keeps dropping banana skins round here?" growled the lion.

"Not me," said the monkey.

"Who keeps walking all over me?" hissed the snake.

"Not me," growled the lion.

"And not me," said the monkey.

"Who keeps throwing coconuts about?" snorted the rhino.

"Not me," hissed the snake.

"Not me," growled the lion.

"And not me," said the monkey.

by Colin West

"WHO KEEPS TICKLING ME?"
 roared the elephant.
"Not me," snorted the rhino.
"Not me," hissed the snake.
"Not me," growled the lion.
"And not ME!" said the monkey.

Slurp! Slurp! Slurp! went the elephant.

WHOOOOSH!

"Now who's going to stop all this monkey business?"
 laughed the lion, and the snake,
 and the rhino,
 and the elephant.

"Well…
NOT ME!" said You-Know-Who.

183

THE ELEPHANT TREE
by Penny Dale

Elephant wanted to climb a tree. So we went to find the elephant tree.

We walked and we walked. We looked and we looked.

"Is this the elephant tree?" "No," said the birds. "It's the bird tree."

"Is this the elephant tree?" "No," said the monkeys. "It's the monkey tree."

"Is this the elephant tree?"

"No," said the tigers.

"It's the tiger tree."

"Are any of these the elephant tree?"

"No," said the bears. "These are bear trees."

We ran and we ran.

We walked and we walked.

We looked and we looked.

But we still couldn't find the elephant tree.

Never mind, Elephant. Wait and see.

Here it is. Look. The elephant tree.

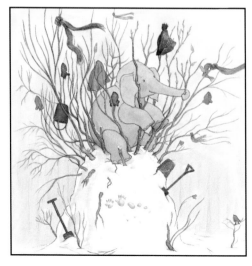

185

MY FRIEND HARRY

The day James bought Harry, Harry's life changed. James talked all the way home. Harry didn't say a thing. He just sat in the car, looking clean and new and neat.

"What are you thinking?" James asked. But Harry never said.

At the beginning of every day, when James woke up, he tossed and rumpled the blankets until Harry fell out of bed.

"Good morning, my friend Harry!" James said. "What shall we do today?" But Harry never said.

BY KIM LEWIS

So in the mornings, James and Harry went everywhere. They climbed to the top of the hill and back again, and travelled from one end of the farm to the other.

In the sun and the wind and the rain, Harry's skin soon began to wrinkle. Once he fell off James' bicycle and James had to mend his head.

In the afternoons James and Harry helped his father and mother – gathering sheep, feeding cattle, fixing tractors and bringing in the hay.

Both James and Harry got very dirty. After many bathtimes Harry's jacket shrank and his skin began to fade.

"What are you thinking?" James asked Harry.

But Harry never said, so James hugged him tight until Harry's ears began to flop and his trunk began to sag.

Sometimes James made Harry stand on his head. Harry never complained.

"My friend Harry!" James always said.

At the end of every day James tucked Harry into bed beside him. He read story after story and talked and talked.

"Are you listening?" he yawned.

But Harry lay close to James and never said, until James' dad came in to kiss them.

James even took Harry on holiday, squeezing him into the dark in a bag with the apple juice. But the juice spilled and made Harry very sticky. James scrubbed Harry and hung him out to dry. Harry swung in the sea breeze, while James and his mum and dad ran in and out of the waves.

Then one day Harry could no longer sit up straight. James propped him up in a chair.

"I'm going to school today!" James said. "What do you think?"

Harry was quiet. James got dressed in brand new clothes, and went a little quiet too.

Harry stayed cuddled up in James' mother's arms while the children played all around in the school yard. When James went into school, his mother waved, then drove home, very quietly, with Harry.

James' mother tucked Harry into James' bed and softly closed the door. Harry lay very still. Cows mooed faintly in the distance. James' father drove the tractor out of the yard. Birds pecked and peeped in the bushes by the house. The sun rose up and went round, warming Harry where he lay, until it was afternoon.

Harry lay still, waiting all by himself, without James.

That night, James told Harry about his day. "I expect I'll go to school again tomorrow," he said.

Harry was very quiet.

James stared into the dark for a long time. "Did you miss me, my friend Harry?" he asked.

The next day, James took Harry to school. "Just this once," he said. "Until you get used to being on your own."

Harry sat very close to James and never said a word.

"My friend Harry," said James.

PROWLPUSS

by Gina Wilson
illustrated by David Parkins

Prowlpuss is cunning
   and wily and sly,
A kingsize cat with
   one ear and one eye.
He's not a
   sit-by-the-fire-
   and-purr cat,
A look-at-my-
   exquisite-fur cat,
No, he's not!

He's rough and gruff
   and very very tough.
Where ya goin',
   Prowlpuss?
AHA!

Down in the alley
   something stirs!
Is it a burglar?
Is it a witch?

Is it a ghoul with
   a bag of bones?
No, it's not!
It's Prowlpuss!

He's not a lap cat,
   a cuddle-up-
   for-a-chat cat,
No, he's not!

He's not a sit-in-
   the-window-
   and-stare cat.
He's an I-WAS-
   THERE! cat.

Watch out!
Prowlpuss about!

He's not a stay-
   at-home cat,
No, he's not!

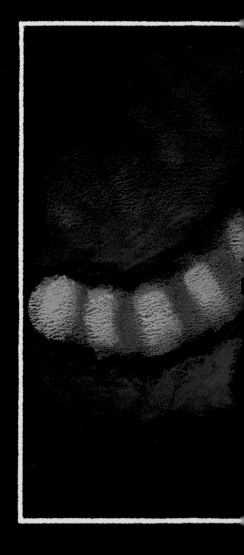

He's not a sit-on-
   the-mat-and-lick-
   yourself-down cat.
He's an out-on-
   the-town cat,
A racer, a chaser,
A "You're a disgrace"-er!
A "Don't show
   your face"-er!

He's not a throat-
    soft-as-silk cat,
A saucer-of-
    milk cat,
No, he's not!
He's a fat cat,
A rat cat,
A "What on earth
    was that?" cat.

So what's it all for –
All the razzle and dazzle,
The crash, bang, wallop,
The yowling,
    the howling,
The "Give us a break!"
"Don't keep us awake!"
"Hoppit!" "Clear off!"
    "Get lost!" "Scram!"

"Good riddance!"
    "Go to the devil!"?

Who is
    he wooing
With his
    hullabalooing
Night after night?

AHA!

Back through
the alley
slinks Prowlpuss
at dawn,
Love-lost and lorn.

And old
Nellie Smith
in her deep
feather bed
Lifts her head.

"That's Prowly
come home!
That's my
jowly Prowly!
My sweet
Prowly-wowly!
My sleep-all-
the-day cat,
My let-the-mice-
play cat,
My what-did-
you-say? cat,
My soft and dozy,
Oh-so-cosy,
Tickle-my-toes-y,
Stroke-my-nose-y

PROWLPUSS."

High in a tree
at the alley's end,
Right at the top
so no one
can get her
Or fret her
or pet her,
Lives one little cat –
A tiny-white-star cat,
A twinkle-afar cat.

In the moonlight
she dances,
Like snowflakes
on branches,
She spins
and she whirls.

But not for long!
In a flash
she's gone!

Now Prowlpuss
will sing for her –
What he would
bring for her!
Oh, how he
longs for her!
Love of his life!

If she'd *only*
come down…

But she won't!
No, she won't!

SQUEAK-A-LOT

In an old old house lived a small small mouse
who had no one to play with.
So the small small mouse went out of the house
to find a friend to play with.

And he found **a bee**.
"Can I play with you?"
the mouse asked the bee.
"Of course," said the bee.
"What will we play?" asked the mouse.
"We'll play Buzz-a-lot," said the bee.

Buzz buzz buzz buzz!

But the mouse didn't like it a lot.
So he went to find a better friend to play with.

And he found **a dog**.
"Can I play with you?" the mouse asked the dog.
"Of course," said the dog.
"What will we play?" asked the mouse.
"We'll play Woof-a-lot," said the dog.

Woof woof woof woof!

But the mouse didn't like it a lot.
So he went to find a better friend to play with.

by **Martin Waddell**
illustrated by **Virginia Miller**

And he found **a chicken**.

"Can I play with you?" the mouse asked the chicken.
"Of course," said the chicken.
"What will we play?" asked the mouse.
"We'll play Cluck-a-lot," said the chicken.

Cluck cluck cluck cluck!

But the mouse didn't like it a lot.
So he went to find a better friend to play with.

And he found **a cat**.
"Can I play with you?"
the mouse asked
the cat. And …

WHAM!

BAM!

SCRAM!

The mouse didn't like
it a lot. So he ran away
through the long long grass
playing Squeak-a-lot all by himself.

Squeak squeak squeak squeak!

Squeak! Some mice found the mouse.
"Can we play with you?" the mice
asked the mouse.
"Of course," said the mouse.
"What will we play?" asked the mice.

"Buzz-a-lot!" said the mouse.

Buzz buzz buzz buzz!

And all of them liked it a lot.

"Woof-a-lot!" said the mouse.

Woof woof woof woof!

And all of them liked it a lot.

"Cluck-a-lot!" said the mouse.

Cluck cluck cluck cluck!

And all of them liked it a lot.

"**WHAM! BAM! SCRAM!**" said the mouse.

The mouse chased the mice through the long long grass back home to the old old house. And together they played …

Sleep-a-lot.

The Big Big Sea

by **Martin Waddell**

illustrated by **Jennifer Eachus**

Mum said, "Let's go!"
So we went
    out of the house
      and into the dark
      and I saw…
THE MOON.

We went over the field
and under the fence
and I saw
the sea in the moonlight,
waiting for me.
Mum said,
"Take off your shoes
and socks!"
And I did.

And I ran
and Mum ran.
We ran and we ran
straight through
the puddles
and out to the sea!

I went right in
to the shiny bit.
There was only me
in the big big sea.

I splashed
and I laughed
and Mum came after me
and we paddled
out deep in the water.

We got all wet.

Then we walked
a bit more
by the edge of the sea
and our feet
made big holes
in the sand.

Far far away
right round the bay
were the town
and the lights
and the mountains.
We felt very small,
Mum and me.

We didn't go to the town.
We just stayed for a while
by the sea.

And Mum said to me,
"Remember this time.
It's the way life should be."

I got cold
and Mum carried me
all the way back.

We sat by the fire,
Mum and me,
and ate hot buttered toast
and I went to sleep
on her knee.

I'll always remember
just Mum and me
and the night
    that we walked
      by the big big sea.

GINGER

by Charlotte Voake

Ginger was a lucky cat. He lived with a little girl who made him delicious meals and gave him a beautiful basket, where he would curl up ... and close his eyes.

Here he is, fast asleep.

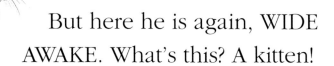

But here he is again, WIDE AWAKE. What's this? A kitten!

"He'll be a nice new friend for you, Ginger," said the little girl. But Ginger didn't want a new friend, especially one like this. Ginger hoped the kitten would go away, but he didn't.

Everywhere Ginger went, the kitten followed, springing out from behind doors, leaping on to Ginger's back, even eating Ginger's food! What a naughty kitten!

But what upset Ginger more than anything was that whenever he got into his beautiful basket, the kitten always climbed in too, and the little girl didn't do anything about it.

So Ginger decided to leave home.

He went out through the cat flap and he didn't come back.

The kitten waited for a bit, then he got into Ginger's basket.

It wasn't the same without Ginger.

The kitten played with some
flowers, then he found somewhere
to sharpen his claws. The little girl found
him on the table drinking some milk.
"You naughty kitten!" she said. "I thought
you were with Ginger. Where is he
anyway?" She looked in Ginger's basket,
but of course he wasn't there. "Perhaps
he's eating his food," she said. But Ginger
wasn't there either. "I hope he's not
upset," she said. "I hope he hasn't run away."

She put on her wellingtons and went out into the
garden, and that is where she found
him; a very wet, sad, cold
Ginger, hiding
under a bush.

The little girl carried Ginger and the kitten inside.
"It's a pity you can't be friends," she said.

She gave Ginger a special meal. She gave the kitten a little
plate of his own. Then she tucked Ginger
into his own warm basket.

All she could find for the kitten to
sleep in was a little tiny cardboard
box. But the kitten didn't mind,
because cats love cardboard boxes
(however small they are).

So when the little girl went in to
see the two cats again, THIS is how
she found them.

And now Ginger and the naughty
kitten get along very well …

most of the time!

TURNOVER TUESDAY

by Phyllis Root
illustrated by Helen Craig

One Tuesday Bonnie Bumble baked six plum turnovers for breakfast. "Delicious," she said, and she ate up five, every bite. There wasn't even a crumb left over for her little dog, Spot.

But when Bonnie Bumble got up from her chair,
she turned over
upside down.

And nothing could turn her back over again.

So Bonnie Bumble put her hat on her feet and her shoes on her hands. Then she went to do her chores.

Upside down she milked the cow.
But the milk SPLASHED out of the bucket.

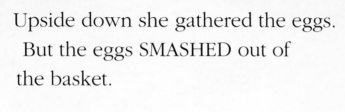

Upside down she gathered the eggs.
But the eggs SMASHED out of
the basket.

On the way back to the house, the sheep nibbled
her hair. And the pig's tail tickled her ear.

"This will never do!" said
Bonnie Bumble.

Back into the kitchen she
went to find the last plum turnover.
Upside down she ate it, almost every bite.

When she got up from the table,
she turned back over, right side up!
"Thank goodness everything's back to
normal," said Bonnie Bumble.
And it was …

except for Spot, who had eaten
up all the crumbs.

Baby Duck
and the
New Eyeglasses

by **Amy Hest**

illustrated by

Jill Barton

Baby Duck was looking in the mirror. She was trying on her new eyeglasses. They were too big on her baby face. They pushed against her baby cheeks. And she did not look like Baby.

Baby came slowly down the stairs.

"Park time!" said Mr Duck. "Grandpa will be waiting in his boat at the lake!"

"How sweet you look in your new eyeglasses!" cooed Mrs Duck. "Don't you love them?"

"No," Baby said.

"How well you must see in your new eyeglasses!" clucked Mr Duck. "Don't you like them just a little?"

"No," Baby said.

The Duck family went out of the front door. Mr and Mrs Duck hopped along. "Hop down the lane, Baby!"

Baby did not hop. Her glasses might fall off.

Mr and Mrs Duck danced along.

"Dance down the lane, Baby!"

Baby did not dance.

Her glasses might fall off.

When they got to the park, Baby sat in the grass behind a tree. She sang a little song.

"Poor, poor Baby, she looks ugly
In her bad eyeglasses.
Everyone can play but me,
Poor, poor, poor, poor Baby."

Grandpa came up the hill. "Where's that Baby?" he called.

"I'm afraid she is hiding," Mrs Duck sighed.

"She does not like her new eyeglasses," worried Mr Duck.

Grandpa sat in the grass behind the tree. "I like your hiding place," he whispered.

"Thank you," Baby said.

Grandpa peered round the side of the tree. "I see new eyeglasses," he whispered. "Are they blue?"

"No," Baby said.

"Green?" Grandpa whispered.

"No," Baby said.

"Cocoa brown?" Grandpa whispered.

Baby came out from behind the tree.

Grandpa folded his arms. "Well," he said, "I think those eyeglasses are *very* fine."

"Why?" Baby asked.

"Because they are red like mine!" Grandpa said.

Grandpa kissed Baby's cheek. "Can you still run to the lake and splash about?"

Baby ran and splashed. Then she splashed harder. Her glasses did not fall off.

"Can you still twirl three times without falling down?"

Baby twirled. One, two, three. She did not fall down. And her glasses did not fall off.

"Come with me, Baby. I have a surprise," Grandpa said.

They walked down to the pier. Grandpa's boat was bobbing on the water. There was another boat, too.

"Can you read what it says?" Grandpa asked.

Baby read, "B-a-b-y."

The letters were very clear. Then Grandpa and Mr and Mrs Duck sat in Grandpa's boat.

But Baby sat in *her* boat and
sang a new song.

"I have nice new eyeglasses!
I look like my grandpa.
My rowing-boat is lots of fun,
And I can read my name on it."

CALAMITY

James and Horatio were building a tower.

"One, two, three," said James as he balanced the blocks.

"Seven, four," added Horatio.

"HEE-HAW!" BUMP! Something crashed into the Useful Box and sent everything flying.

"What was that?" asked Horatio.

"It's a calamity," said James, looking at the mess.

"What were you doing, Calamity?" asked Horatio.

"Racing," Calamity said. "And I won."

"Can I race?" asked Horatio.

"Find yourself a jockey," Calamity said. "Here's mine." She turned round.

But that's a bobbin, thought James. He started to tidy up.

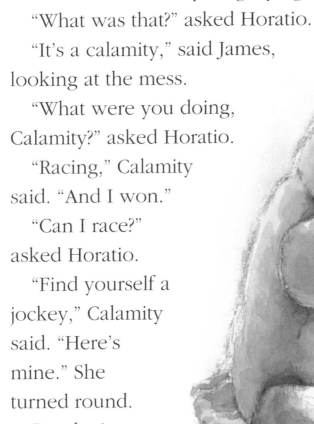

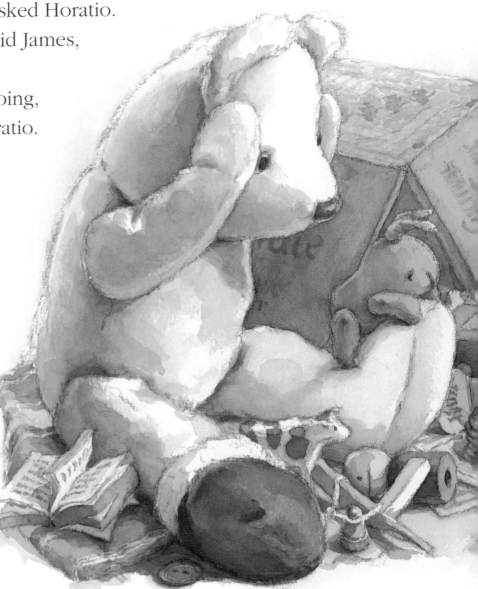

210

by Camilla Ashforth

Horatio looked for a jockey. I like this one, he thought. It was James's clock.

"Are you ready?" asked Calamity.

They waited a moment.

"One, two, three, go!" Calamity called. She hurtled round the Useful Box. Twice.

Horatio tried to move his jockey.

He pushed it and pulled it. Then he rolled it over. His jockey would not budge.

Calamity screeched to a halt. "Hee-haw! I won!" she bellowed. "Let's race again."

James turned round. He picked up Horatio's jockey.

"That's my clock," said James and he put it in his Useful Box. Horatio looked for another jockey.

"One, two, three, go!" Calamity called. She galloped very fast. Backwards and forwards.

Horatio looked around. I'll go this way, he thought, and he set off with his new jockey.

"Hee-haw! Won again!" cried Calamity, stopping suddenly.

Horatio looked puzzled.

"One more race," Calamity said. "I'm good at this."

"James," whispered Horatio, "can you help me win this time?"

"What you need is a race track," said James. "I'll make you one. This block is the start," he said. "And this string is the finishing line. Ready, steady, go!"

Calamity thundered off. She was going the wrong way.

Horatio headed for the finishing line as fast as he could.

Calamity turned in a circle and headed back towards James.

"Stop!"
James cried.
 As Horatio crossed the line,
Calamity collided with the Useful Box. CRASH!
 "That was a good race. Who won?" asked Calamity.
 "I think you both did," James said, and squeezed Horatio tight.

213

Bathwater's Hot

by Shirley Hughes

Bathwater's hot,
  Seawater's cold,
Ginger's kittens are *very* young
  But Buster's getting old.

Some things you can throw away,
   Some are nice to keep.
Here's someone who is wide awake,
     Shhh, he's fast asleep!

Some things are hard as stone,
   Some are soft as cloud.
Whisper very quietly…
   SHOUT OUT LOUD!

It's fun to run very fast
   Or to be slow.
The red light says 'stop'
   And the green light says 'go'.

It's kind to be helpful,
   Unkind to tease,
Rather rude to push and grab,
   Polite to say 'please'.

Night time is dark,
   Day time is light.
The sun says 'good morning'
   And the moon says 'good night'.

Good night !

Grandad's Magic

by Bob Graham

Three dogs lived in Alison's house. Two sat high on the shelf. They were very precious to Alison's mum. They were very breakable. Alison was not to touch them even if she could reach. She didn't like them anyway.

Alison much preferred Rupert. He lived on the armchair. Rupert only left the chair to have his dinner or go to the toilet. He wouldn't leave the chair for Alison's mum *or* her dad, and certainly not for Max, who often tried to pull his tail.

Rupert wouldn't even get out of his chair when Grandma and Grandad came to lunch on Sunday. Alison held Max for Grandma to kiss. He curled his fists and kicked his legs.

"Give him to me," said Grandad. "I know how to handle this young chap. Now for my magic…"

Grandad reached into Max's shirt and slowly pulled out a chocolate bear.

"Have you been keeping that in your shirt all this time?" he said. Max's face lit up with pleasure. Then Grandad lost the bear … and found it again under Rupert's collar!

"It's magic," said Alison.

"Watch me, Grandad," said Alison. She had a trick of her own. She was learning to juggle with three puffins filled with sand that Grandad had given her. This *sounded* easy, but she

had to keep them going from hand to hand. The idea was to have three puffins in the air all at once.

"Try one at a time, Alison," said Grandad. "Backwards and forwards, and when you

learn that, try two, and when you learn that, try three."

"I'm not as good as I used to be," said Grandad.

Sunday was the only day the china dogs came down from the shelf. Alison's mum used them as a table decoration. They guarded the fruit. Every Sunday Grandad picked his table napkin out of the air like an apple off a tree. And he talked of his best trick of all …

"I used to be able to take this tablecloth, give it a pull in a certain kind of way, and it would whip out from under all this stuff and leave everything standing there. But that was a long time ago."

Then one Sunday, Grandad noticed how well Alison juggled, and …

without warning, he removed his coat and climbed on to the chair.

"One good trick deserves another," he said. And he gave the tablecloth a short, snapping tug.

There was a moment of silence. Mum looked pale.

"You did it!" said Alison.
Grandad did a triumphant dance round the room. And *that's* when it happened.

An orange rolled off the bowl, hit one of the precious dogs and sent it spinning

into mid-air … just as Rupert happened to be making a trip to the toilet. It settled on his very broad back …

then landed safely in Max's lap. Alison held her breath. Would Grandad get into trouble? But Mum smiled thinly as she put the dogs back on the shelf.

"Don't *you* try that trick, Ally," said Grandad.

The following Sunday there were a number of changes in Alison's house. When Grandma and Grandad came to lunch, the dogs stayed on the shelf. And the table was set with unbreakable plastic plates and place mats.

Just before lunch, Rupert found a box of chocolates hidden under his cushion.

Later, Grandad made the chocolates appear just like magic. They were for Mum, who had such a shock last week.

Alison was dismayed. "That's not magic, it's a trick! You put them there, Grandad. The price is still on them!"

"We performers can't get it right all the time, Alison," Grandad said, "but the chocolates have certainly vanished.

Now let's see how long *you* can spin this plastic plate on the end of your finger!"

YOU AND ME, LITTLE BEAR

by
Martin Waddell

illustrated by
Barbara Firth

Once there were two bears, Big Bear and Little Bear. Big Bear is the big bear and Little Bear is the little bear.

Little Bear wanted to play, but Big Bear had things to do.
"I want to play!" Little Bear said.
"I've got to get wood for the fire," said Big Bear.
"I'll get some too," Little Bear said.
"You and me, Little Bear," said Big Bear. "We'll fetch the wood in together!"

"What shall we do now?" Little Bear asked.

"I'm going for water," said Big Bear.
"Can I come too?" Little Bear asked.
"You and me, Little Bear," said Big Bear. "We'll go for the water together."

"Now we can play," Little Bear said.
"I've still got to tidy our cave," said Big Bear.
"Well … I'll tidy too!" Little Bear said.
"You and me," said Big Bear. "You tidy your things, Little Bear. I'll look after the rest."

"I've tidied my things, Big Bear!" Little Bear said.
"That's good, Little Bear," said Big Bear. "But I'm not finished yet."
"I want you to play!" Little Bear said.
"You'll have to play by yourself, Little Bear," said Big Bear. "I've still got plenty to do!"

Little Bear went to play by himself, while Big Bear got on with the work.

Little Bear
played bear-jump.
Little Bear played bear-slide. Little Bear played bear-swing. Little Bear played bear-tricks-with-bear-sticks. Little Bear played bear-stand-on-his-head and Big Bear came out to sit on his rock. Little Bear played bear-run-about-by-himself and Big Bear closed his eyes for a think.

Little Bear went to speak to Big Bear, but Big Bear was … asleep!
"Wake up, Big Bear!" Little Bear said. Big Bear opened his eyes. "I've played all my games by myself," Little Bear said.

Big Bear thought for a bit, then he said, "Let's play hide-and-seek, Little Bear."
"I'll hide and you seek," Little Bear said, and he ran off to hide.
"I'm coming now!" Big Bear called, and he looked till he found Little Bear. Then Big Bear hid, and Little Bear looked.

"I found you, Big Bear!" Little Bear said. "Now I'll hide again."

They played lots of bear-games. When the sun slipped away through the trees, they were still playing. Then Little Bear said, "Let's go home now, Big Bear."

Big Bear and Little Bear went home to their cave.
"We've been busy today, Little Bear!" said Big Bear.
"It was lovely, Big Bear," Little Bear said. "Just you and me playing …

together."

The Teeny Tiny WOMAN

A Traditional Tale
illustrated by **Arthur Robins**

Once upon a time a teeny tiny woman who lived in a teeny tiny house put on her teeny tiny hat and went out for a teeny tiny walk.

When the teeny tiny woman had gone a teeny tiny way, she went through a teeny tiny gate into a teeny tiny churchyard.

In the teeny tiny churchyard the teeny tiny woman found a teeny tiny bone on a teeny tiny grave. Then the teeny tiny woman said to her teeny tiny self, "This teeny tiny bone will make some teeny tiny soup for my teeny tiny supper."

So the teeny tiny woman took the teeny tiny bone back to her teeny tiny house. When she got home she felt a teeny tiny tired, so she put the teeny tiny bone in her teeny tiny cupboard and got into her teeny tiny bed for a teeny tiny sleep.

After a teeny tiny while the teeny tiny woman was woken by a teeny tiny voice that said, "Give me my bone!"

The teeny tiny woman was a teeny tiny frightened, so she hid her teeny tiny head under her teeny tiny sheet.

The teeny tiny voice said a teeny tiny closer and a teeny tiny louder, **"Give me my bone!"**

This made the teeny tiny woman a teeny tiny more frightened, so she hid her teeny tiny head a teeny tiny further under her teeny tiny sheet.

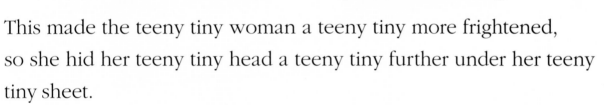

Then the teeny tiny voice said a teeny tiny closer and a teeny tiny louder, **"Give me my bone!"**

The teeny tiny woman was a teeny tiny more frightened, but she put her teeny tiny head out from under her teeny tiny sheet and said in her **loudest** teeny tiny voice …

225

"TAKE IT!"

That's the Way to Do It!

by Colin McNaughton

There was an old woman
 Who lived in a shoe,
She had so many children
 She didn't know what to do;
So she sought the advice
 Of her friend Mr Punch,
Who said fry them with onions
 And eat them for lunch!

Friends

by Kim Lewis

Sam's friend Alice came to play on the farm. They were in the garden when they heard loud clucking coming from the hen house.

"Listen!" said Sam. "That means a hen has laid an egg."

"An egg!" said Alice. "Let's go and find it."

Sam and Alice ran to the hen house.

"Look," said Alice. "There's the egg!"

"I can put it in my hat," said Sam.

"I can put your hat in my bucket,"

said Alice, "and put the bucket in the wheelbarrow."

"Then we can take it home," said Sam.

The geese stood across the path.

"I'm afraid of geese," said Alice.

"Come on," said Sam. "We can go the long way round."

Alice pushed the wheelbarrow through the trees.

"It's my turn now," said Sam, and he pulled it through the long grass and thistles.

Together, they lifted it over a ditch.

Sam and Alice went into the barn. They were followed by Glen, the old farm dog.

"Is the egg all right?" asked Alice.

Sam and Alice looked in the hat. The egg was safe and smooth, without a crack.

"Look what we've found!" said Alice, holding out the egg to Glen.

"No!" cried Sam. "He'll eat it!"

Sam reached out to take the egg.

Alice held it tight.

"It's mine!" said Sam.

"It's not!" said Alice. "I found it!"

"They're my hens!" said Sam, pushing Alice.

Just then loud clucking came from the hen house. Sam ran out of the barn.

"Another egg!" he cried.

Sam and Alice looked at each other.

"We can go and find it," said Sam.

"Yes, let's!" said Alice, and smiled.

SMASH went the egg as it fell on the ground. Glen started to eat it.

"I don't like you any more," said Alice. She picked up her bucket and went out of the barn.

Sam put on his empty hat. He did like Alice and he didn't like Alice and he felt he was going to cry.

Sam put the egg in his hat. He gave the hat to Alice who put it in her bucket. They tiptoed past the geese and Glen and walked back to the house.

"What have you two been doing?" asked Mum.

"Finding eggs," said Sam.

"Together!" said Alice.

233

Mimi and the Blackberry Pies

by Martin Waddell illustrated by Leo Hartas

Mimi lived with her mouse sisters and brothers beneath the big tree. It was blackberry time in the hedge.

"I'm going to make blackberry pies," Mimi told her mouse sisters.

"We'll help you, Mimi!" her mouse sisters said. "We'll pick the best berries to go in the pies!" They all loved Mimi's blackberry pies.

Mimi's mouse sisters took their baskets out to the hedge, and they started to pick the juicy blackberries, but the berries were nice and they ate a lot more than they picked.

They ate and they ate

and they ate

and they ate

and they ate

and they ate. But they didn't pick many berries for Mimi.

"This isn't much help!" Mimi said, when she'd counted the berries they'd picked.

"We'll help you, Mimi," her mouse brothers cried. "We'll pick trillions of berries!" They all loved Mimi's blackberry pies.

Mimi's mouse brothers climbed up into the hedge and got busy. But soon some-brother-mouse splatted some-other-brother-mouse with a berry! Mouse-brother-splatting looked fun. They forgot all about picking berries for Mimi, and started mouse-splatting each other instead.

They splatted

and they splatted

and they splatted

and they splatted

and they splatted.

But they didn't pick many berries for Mimi.

"This isn't much help!" Mimi sighed. And she went out to the hedge and picked all the berries she needed herself.

Mimi made blackberry pies. A sweet berry smell drifted over Mimi's sisters and brothers.

Their noses twitched

and they twitched

and they twitched

and they twitched

and they twitched.

The rich berry smell was so good that Mimi's sisters and brothers ran to her house. Mimi came out with the pies that she'd made on a tray. Mimi's blackberry pies were bursting with berries and juice.

"This time I'm sure that you'll help!" Mimi said. And her mouse sisters and brothers helped Mimi eat all her blackberry pies!

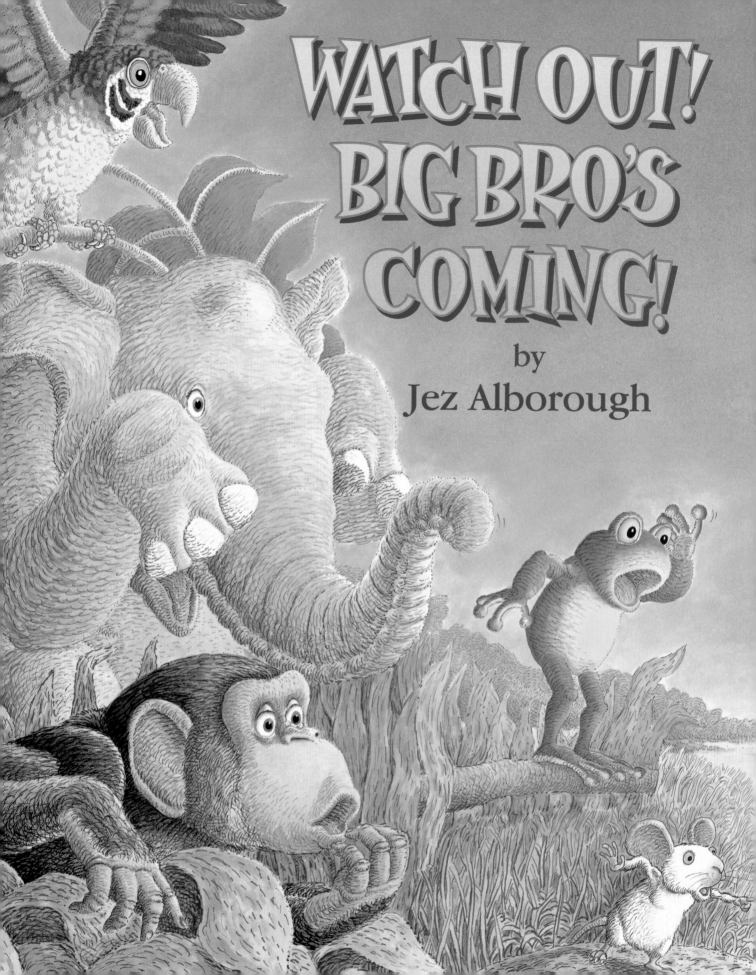

WATCH OUT! BIG BRO'S COMING!

by

Jez Alborough

"Help!" squeaked a mouse. "He's coming!"

"Who's coming?" asked a frog.

"Big Bro," said the mouse. "He's rough, he's tough, and he's big."

"Big?" said the frog. "How big?"

The mouse stretched out his arms as wide as they could go. "This big," he cried, and he scampered off to hide.

"Look out!" croaked the frog. "Big Bro's coming!"

"Big who?" asked the parrot.

"Big Bro," said the frog. "He's rough, he's tough, and he's really big."

"Really big?" said the parrot. "How big?"

The frog stretched out his arms as wide as they could go. "This big," he cried, and he hopped off to hide.

"Watch out!" squawked the parrot. "Big Bro's coming!"

"Who's he?" asked the chimpanzee.

"Don't you know Big Bro?" asked the parrot. "He's rough, he's tough, and he's ever so big."

"Ever so big?" said the chimpanzee. "How big?"

The parrot stretched out his wings as wide as they could go. "This big," he cried, and he flapped off to hide.

"Ooh-ooh! Look out!" whooped the chimpanzee. "Big Bro's coming!"

"Big Joe?" said the elephant.

"No," said the chimpanzee. "Big Bro. He's rough, he's tough, and everybody knows how big Big Bro is."

The elephant shook his head. "I don't," he said.

The chimpanzee stretched out his arms as wide as they could go. "This big," he cried.

"That big?" gulped the elephant. "Let's hide!"

So there they all were, hiding and waiting, waiting and hiding.

"Where is he?" asked the elephant.

"Shhh," said the chimpanzee. "I don't know."

"Why don't you creep out and have a look around?" whispered the elephant.

"Not me," said the chimpanzee.

"Not me," said the parrot.

"Not me," said the frog.

"All right," said the mouse. "As you're all so frightened, I'll go."

The mouse tiptoed ever so slowly out from his hiding place. He looked this way and that way to see if he could see Big Bro.

And then … "He's coming!" shrieked the mouse.

"H … h … h … hide!"

Big Bro came closer and closer and closer. Everyone covered their eyes.

"Oh no," whispered the frog.

"Help," gasped the parrot.

"I can hear something coming," whined the chimpanzee.

"It's him," whimpered the elephant. "*It's … it's …*"

"**BIG BRO!**" shrieked the mouse.

"Is that Big Bro?" asked the frog.

"He's tiny," said the parrot.

"Teeny weeny," said the chimpanzee.

"He's a mouse," said the elephant.

Big Bro looked up at them all, took a deep breath, and said …

"BOO!"

"Come on,
Little Bro," said
Big Bro. "Mum wants you back
home *now!*"

   "Wow," said the elephant.
   "Phew," said the chimpanzee.
   "He is rough," said the parrot.
   "And tough," said the frog.
   "Rough and tough," said
Little Bro, looking
back over his
shoulder.

"And I *told* you he was big!"

Oh, Tucker!

by Steven Kroll
illustrated by Scott Nash

"**TUCKER!** Time for breakfast!"
Tina called.

Tucker came running.
WHAM! He
knocked over
a dustbin.

He jumped
up and licked
Tina's chin.
    "Oh, Tucker!" Tina giggled.

Tucker pushed open the front door
and raced into the house.
WHAM! He
knocked over a
vase of flowers.
WHAM! He
    knocked a china
        plate on to the floor.
            "Oh, Tucker!" Tina groaned.

        Tucker ran for the stairs.
        "Tucker, no!" Tina cried.
    "It's breakfast-time!"
        But Tucker didn't listen. He had

to say good morning to Tina's parents.
            He bounded up the stairs.

        Mum and Dad were fast
        asleep. Tucker didn't mind.
    WHAM! He landed on
    the bed.

        "OOF!" said Mum.
        "OOF!" said Dad.

Tucker licked their faces and wagged
his tail. **WHAM!** He knocked over the
bedside lamp. **WHAM!** He knocked
    over the clock and the radio and a
    glass of water.
        "Oh, Tucker!" said Tina.

Tucker barked. He ran back to the
stairs – and
slipped!

Tucker flew
through
the air.

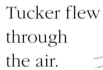

240

WHAM! He hit the wall and a picture fell. He scrambled to his feet. WHAM! He knocked over a table and a lamp. The lampshade plopped on his head.

Tucker couldn't see but that didn't stop him. He zigzagged through the living room.

"Oh, Tucker, WAIT!" Tina cried. But Tucker didn't listen.

WHAM! He knocked over a chair. WHAM! He knocked over a vase. WHAM! He knocked over a plant and a bowl and a china cat.

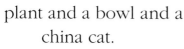

WHAM! WHAM! WHAM!

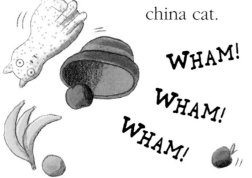

Tucker stepped on Tina's skateboard and zoomed down the hall! Tina hid her eyes. "Oh, Tucker!"

WHAM! He crashed against the kitchen sink. The lampshade flew off his head. Tina hurried in. Mum and Dad hurried in, too.

"Here, Tucker, look," Tina said. She set his dish down in front of him. They all held their breath. Tucker dug in. "Finally," said Tina.

Mum and Dad sighed with relief. Tina smiled. Such a nice dog. Such a friendly dog. Who could possibly scold him?

WHAM! WHAM! WHAM! WHAM! WHAM! WHAM! WHAM!

"Oh, Tucker!"

A Friend for Little Bear

by Harry Horse

L ittle Bear lived all alone on a desert island. "I wish I had something to play with," he said.

A stick came floating by. Little Bear picked it out of the sea. He drew a picture in the sand. Then he drew some more. "I need something else to play with," he said. He was tired of drawing pictures.

A bottle came floating by. Little Bear picked it out of the sea. He filled it up with water, then poured out the water on the sand.

"I need a cup," said Little Bear, "to pour the water into."

242

Then something spotted came floating by. Little Bear wondered what it was. "It isn't a cup," he said, but he pulled it out of the sea anyway. It was a wooden horse.

The wooden horse ran round the island. Little Bear ran after him. The wooden horse hid. Little Bear looked for him. They had a lovely time. They drew pictures in the sand and filled the bottle again and again. They played all day long and

then went to sleep under the tall palm tree.

Little Bear woke up. He rubbed his eyes. "Look!" he cried. "Lots of things floating in the water!" He stretched with his stick and pulled out as many as he could. "I don't know what these things are," he said, "but I need them, all the same." He piled them into a heap. Then he sighed. "I still do wish I had a cup."

There wasn't much room on the island now. Little Bear
had filled it up. He told the wooden horse to get
out of the way. "Climb on to that," said Little
Bear. "I need more room for these boxes."

"Look!" cried Little Bear. "A cup!"

SNAP!

The roof broke. The wooden
horse fell into the sea and floated away.

244

Little Bear was filling his bottle with water and pouring the water into his cup. "Watch me!" he cried. He filled up the bottle again. "Watch me!" But no one was there. He looked up. He put the bottle down. He walked all round the island. "Where are you?" he called. "I need you!" but no one answered.

"I need my *friend*," said Little Bear. "I don't need that cup!" He threw all his things back into the sea and they floated away.

He sat underneath the tall palm tree and began to cry.

ittle Bear dried his eyes. Then he rubbed them. Something spotted was floating by.

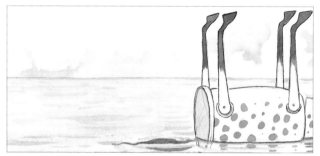

He ran and pulled it out of the sea.

"I only need you, Wooden Horse," he said, and the two of them danced for joy on the sand.

245

Pog had by Peter Haswell

Pog had a banana. "I wonder what a banana does," said Pog.

He put it on his head.  It fell off.

He dropped it on the floor.

 It didn't bounce.

 He put it in a vase.

 It didn't grow.

Pog peeled the banana.

He threw away 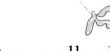 the skin.

Pog walked…

"Now I know what a banana does," said Pog.

"It makes you fall down!"

What Newt Could Do for Turtle

Written by
Jonathan London

Illustrated by
Louise Voce

Spring had come to the swamp.

A red-spotted newt crawled out from his winter bed in the mud.

"Help!" cried Newt. "I'm stuck!"

A painted turtle yawned, greeting the spring.

"Coming, dear Newt!" cried Turtle.

Pock! went the mud as Turtle pulled Newt free.

"Thanks, Turtle! You're the best!"

"That's what friends are for!" said Turtle.

"Yep," said Newt. His spots turned a deeper red, and he wondered, *What can I do for Turtle?*

That spring the swamp buzzed with life. There were catfish and dragonflies, cat's-tails and dogwoods, polecats and tadpoles. Turtle took good care of Newt, and Newt and Turtle were happy just to be together. But sometimes, when Newt sat alone on his thinking rock, he wondered, *What can I do for Turtle?*

In the summer Newt and Turtle played in their favourite swimming holes.

They swooshed down muddy banks and crashed into the water together – *splash!*

Playing hide-and-seek, Newt climbed on to Turtle's back.
"*Yoo-hoo!* Turtle! Where are you?"
He thought he was on a rock.

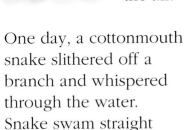

"*Boo!*" said Turtle, poking his head out.
Newt jumped high into the air.

Autumn came and the leaves of the swamp trees sailed down like little umbrellas.

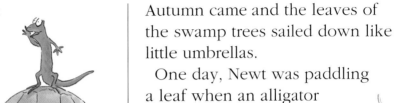

One day, Newt was paddling a leaf when an alligator glided up to him.

Turtle was watching but he was so scared he hit the water with a great *smack!* and went under.
Alligator turned her head to look, and at that moment Newt dived away.

One day, a cottonmouth snake slithered off a branch and whispered through the water. Snake swam straight towards Newt.
He was about to strike when Newt heard Turtle's voice,
"*Newt! A snake!*"

Newt plunged into the water and hid at the bottom of the swamp.
Once again, Newt wondered, *What can I do for Turtle?*

Newt and Turtle hid together beneath the duckweed. Newt sighed, happy to be alive, and his spots turned redder. Now, more than ever, he wondered, *What can I do for Turtle?*

Then, one day, a curious bobcat slunk through the reeds, twitched his whiskers and *pounced* – right on to Turtle's back.
"*Yikes!*" yelled Turtle, pulling his head inside his shell.
Bobcat batted with his paws and flipped Turtle over. Then he grew bored and trotted back into the forest.

249

Poor Turtle wriggled back and forth. If he could not roll over, he would dry up and die!

"Newt, oh Newt!" he cried. "Where are you?"

Now, across the swamp, Newt was dreaming that Turtle was in trouble. "*What can I do for Turtle?*" he said.

His own words woke him up! His heart bumped and stumbled, just like his feet. He scurried to and fro, searching for his friend.

At last, beneath a weeping willow, Newt found him.

"Turtle!" cried Newt. "What are you doing?"

"Pretending I'm a bowl of soup. *What does it look like I'm doing?*"

"Don't worry," said Newt. "I'll help you." This was his big chance! Newt went to his thinking rock, and thought and thought.

"*Aha!*" he said at last. He hauled a big stick over to Turtle and stuck it under his shell.

He pushed a rock beneath the stick then he sprang up, grabbed hold, and swung.

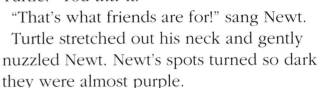

"*Rock 'n' roll!*" cried Newt. Turtle wobbled, teetered on edge …

and toppled over.

"Hooray!" shouted Turtle. "You *did* it!"

"That's what friends are for!" sang Newt.

Turtle stretched out his neck and gently nuzzled Newt. Newt's spots turned so dark they were almost purple.

The days were getting shorter. Ducks splashed off, chattering news of winter.

Newt licked a toe and held it up, testing the breeze. "Yep," he said. "Winter has finally come."

Turtle nodded with a drowsy smile.

"Well," said Newt, "it's nice knowing what we can do for each other."

"Yes," said Turtle wisely, "these things are worth remembering."

"Goodnight, Turtle," said Newt. "See you next spring!"

"Goodnight, Newt!" said Turtle.

And they slipped deep into the swamp mud, where it was snug and cosy and warm.

"Sleep tight!" murmured Turtle.

And that is what they did.

All winter.

Baby Bird

This is the bird that climbed out of the nest and …

CROAK!

flop
flop
flop …
he fell!

This is the squirrel that sniffed at the bird that fell.

This is the bee that buzzed round the bird that fell.

This is the frog that hopped over the bird that fell.

This is the cat that stalked the bird …

and fell himself (which was just as well).

by Joyce Dunbar
illustrated by Russell Ayto

YAWN

This is the dog that opened wide and a bird that nearly walked inside.

A baby bird that wanted to fly up, up above, up above in the sky …
and thought he would have just one more try …

 flap flap  flap flap …

This is the bird that **flew!**

chirp chirp cheep!

COWBOY BABY

SUE HEAP

It was getting late and Sheriff Pa said, "Cowboy Baby, time for bed."

But Cowboy Baby wouldn't go to bed, not without Texas Ted and Denver Dog and Hank the Horse.

"Off you go and find them," said Sheriff Pa. "Bring them safely home."

Cowboy Baby put on his hat and his boots,

and he set off on the trail of Texas Ted, Denver Dog and Hank the Horse. He went down the dusty path and through the barnyard gate.

Over by the hen-house he found ... **Texas Ted.** "Howdy, Texas Ted," said Cowboy Baby.

Cowboy Baby and Texas Ted crossed the rickety bridge.

Down by the old wagon wheel they found ... **Denver Dog.** "Howdy, Denver Dog," said Cowboy Baby.

Cowboy Baby, Texas Ted and Denver Dog crawled through the long grass and out into the big, wide desert.

There by the little rock they found ...

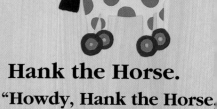

Hank the Horse. "Howdy, Hank the Horse," said Cowboy Baby.

"I'VE FOUND THEM," Cowboy Baby shouted to Sheriff Pa.

"That's dandy," Sheriff Pa called back. "Bring them home now, safe and sound."

Cowboy Baby and his gang sat down on the little rock. None of them wanted to go home.

"Let's hide!" said Cowboy Baby. "Hey, Sheriff Pa," he shouted. "I bet you can't find us, NO SIRREE!"

255

Sheriff Pa came to the big, wide desert.
"Shh!" said Cowboy Baby to his gang.
Sheriff Pa looked. He looked ... and he looked ... and he looked. But he couldn't find Cowboy Baby. No sirree!

"You got me beat, Cowboy Baby," called Sheriff Pa. "But if you come out, there'll be a big surprise, just for you!"
Out jumped Cowboy Baby. "Howdy, Sheriff Pa!"

The sheriff threw his lasso. It twisted and turned in the starlit sky and it caught ... a twinkling star.

"Look!" said Sheriff Pa, and he gave the star to Cowboy Baby. "Now you're my deputy," he said.

Then Cowboy Baby picked up Texas Ted and Denver Dog and Hank the Horse, and Sheriff Pa picked up Cowboy Baby.

And all together they went home to bed.

"Nighty night, Cowboy Baby," said Sheriff Pa. But Cowboy Baby was already fast asleep.

YES SIRREE!

SOMETHING'S COMING!

by Richard Edwards ● *illustrated by* Dana Kubick

"Something's coming!" said Elephant, sitting up.

"Nothing's coming," said Frog sleepily.

"Something's coming," said Elephant.

"Nothing's coming," said Little Rabbit.

"Something's coming," said Elephant.

"Nothing's coming," said Frog and Little Rabbit together.

"I'm sure something's coming," said Elephant.

Little Rabbit pushed back the blanket and looked out of the box.

"If Elephant thinks something's coming, we'll never get any sleep until we've found out what it is. Come on, let's have a look round."

And with the others following close behind, Little Rabbit climbed out of the box and dropped silently to the floor.

It was very quiet in the moonlit room.

They crept to the door and listened, but there was no sound of anything coming. They climbed on to the window-sill and peered out, but there was no sight of anything coming. They looked up the chimney. They looked in the cupboards. They looked under the sofa. They looked everywhere.

"See," said Little Rabbit. "Nothing's coming. Not a single thing."

Elephant raised his trunk. "Something's coming," he insisted. " I can feel it."

"Then what is it?" asked Frog.

"It's a … It's a …

It's a … a … a …

T C H O O !"

And Elephant sneezed so hard that Frog and Little Rabbit went flying across the room and landed in a tangled heap in the corner.

"Is that what was coming?" asked Little Rabbit, picking herself up.

"Yes," said Elephant. "A … a … a … a … TCHOO!" And he sneezed again, even harder than before.

"I knew something was coming," said Elephant, breathing deeply through his nice clear trunk. "Let's go back to bed now."

Soon they were fast asleep.

Nasty Kids, Nice Kids

What are nasty kids like?

They pull your hair,
    they call you names,

They tell you lies,
    they spoil your games,

They draw on walls,
    scream on the floor.

Nasty kids want more, **more, more.**

by Catherine and Laurence Anholt

What are nice kids like?

They make you laugh,
they hold your hand,

Nice kids always
understand.

They share their toys,
they let you play,

They chase the nasty kids away.

Let the Lynx Come In

Jonathan London

∞

illustrated by

Patrick Benson

As the fire snaps
and roars
in the pot-belly stove,
my father snores,
but I can't sleep.
It was his idea
to come
to the north woods
where I've never
been before.

There are wolves
and bears out there.
And a lynx.

I hear a scratching
coming from
outside.

I get up,
creep to the door,
open it a crack,
then jump back ...

A WILDCAT!

The lynx steps in,
shakes first
one paw
then the other;
stands still
as a stone,
quiet as an owl,
in the middle
of the room.
Firelight glows
in its yellow eyes.

I shiver
in the warm room
as the lynx grows
and grows
and grows,
till its whiskers
touch the walls!

Great Lynx
commands
with his silence.

I grab fistfuls of fur
and climb up and up
on to the back
of the enormous cat.
And the next thing
I know ...

we're outside in
the snow!

Bunched like a fist
I clench fur as
Great Lynx creeps
on big cat's feet.
If I cry, my tears
will turn to ice.
In the trees
the moon trembles
on a bare
black branch,
then rolls
along with us
through the hard
northern night.

Great Lynx leaps
across
a frozen river,
steps across
glittering snow,
stalking some
invisible thing.
We climb a ridge
of ice and
there it is!

Great Lynx stops
and crouches.
And together
we watch the
dance of the
northern lights.

In an explosion
of snow
Great Lynx leaps
into the sky!
I cling to the
wildcat's back
as we claw
up and up
the curtains
of light ...
and land with
a pounce
on the big
round moon.

Suddenly
I'm filled with stars
and moonlight.

Great Lynx purrs
and if I could
I would purr too.

I yawn and
drowsily say,
"Lynx, let's go home!"

Down and down
we ripple
through the night,
down the curtains
of light ...
till we flop
like a pile of snow
before my cabin.

I climb off,
turn at the door.
Before my eyes
Great Lynx shrinks
down and down.

He crouches and
I feel his gaze
inside me

like fire
from
the northern lights.

He shakes a paw
and slowly
bounds away
through
the silent night.

The pot-belly's
still chugging.
My dad's
still snoring.

I curl up and
gaze at the fire.
As I close my eyes
and sink
into sleep,
I say ...

"Let the lynx
come in."

And the lynx
sleeps curled
in my dream
like the moon.

NOISY

Noisy noises!

Pan lids clashing,

Dog barking,

Plate smashing,

Telephone ringing,

Baby bawling,

Midnight cats

Cat-a-wauling,

Door slamming,

Aeroplane zooming,

Vacuum cleaner

Vroom-vroom-vrooming,

And if I dance and sing a tune,

Baby joins in with a saucepan and spoon.

by Shirley Hughes

Gentle noises...

Dry leaves swishing,

Falling rain

Splashing, splishing,

Rustling trees

Hardly stirring,

Lazy cat

Softly purring.

Story's over,

Bedtime's come,

Crooning baby

Sucks his thumb.

All quiet, not a peep,

Everyone is fast asleep.

"ONLY JOKING!"
LAUGHED THE LOBSTER
BY COLIN WEST

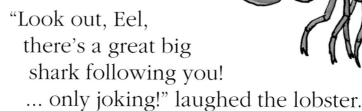

"Look out, Fish, there's a
shark following you!
... only joking!"
laughed the lobster.

"Look out, Eel,
there's a great big
shark following you!
... only joking!" laughed the lobster.

"Look out, Crab, there's a great
big ugly shark following you!
... only joking!" laughed the lobster.

"Look out, Turtle, there's a great big
ugly wild-looking shark following you!
... only joking!" laughed the lobster.

"Look out, Octopus, there's a
great big ugly wild-looking
mean old shark following you!
... only joking!" laughed the lobster.

"Look out, Shark, there's a
great big ugly wild-looking
mean old hungry shark ..."

"SWALLOWING YOU!" said the shark.

And he wasn't joking!

BURP!

One Summer Day

BY KIM LEWIS

One day Max saw a huge red tractor with a plough roar by.

"Go out," said Max, racing to find his shoes and coat and hat. He hurried back to the window and looked out.

Two boys walked along with fishing-rods. Max's friend Sara cycled past in the sun. Max pressed his nose to the window, but the tractor was gone.

As Max looked out, suddenly Sara looked in.

"Peekaboo!" she said.

Then Max heard a knock at the door. "Can Max come out?"

"It's a summer day," laughed Sara, helping Max take off his coat. The sun was hot and the grass smelled sweet. Max and Sara walked down the farm road.

Max and Sara stopped to watch the hens feeding. One hen pecked at Max's foot.

"Shoo!" cried Max and sent the hens flapping.

Max and Sara ran through a field where the grass was very high. A cow with her calf mooed loudly. Max made a small "Moo!" back.

Max and Sara came to the river.

"Look, the boys are fishing." said Sara.

Sara caught Max and took off his shoes before he ran in to paddle.

Then Max and Sara reached a gate. Sara sat Max on top. They heard a roar in the field coming nearer and louder.

"Tractor!" shouted Sara and Max.

Max clung to the gate as the tractor loomed past. It pulled a huge plough which

Sara carried Max back up the road.

"Tractor," sighed Max and closed his eyes.

Max woke up when they reached his house.

"Goodbye, Max," said Sara. "See you soon."

Max raced inside to the window. Sara looked in as Max looked out.

"Peepo!" said Max, and pressed his nose to the glass.

flashed in the sun. The field was full of gulls.

"Let's go home," said Sara to Max.

They walked beside the freshly ploughed field, along by the river and through the grass.

Danny's Duck

A duck flew over the land, looking for a good woody place. Down she flew to a pile of brushwood at the edge of a school playground. No one saw her come.

Except Danny.

At playtime he looked for her.
He had to look hard. Her colours were so like the colours of the twigs and branches.
But Danny saw her.
And she saw him.

by *June Crebbin* • *illustrated by Clara Vulliamy*

In school Danny drew the duck sitting.

"How lovely," said his teacher. "A duck on her nest."

When Danny visited the pile of brushwood again, the duck was still there, sitting very still. Again she saw him. Then she stood up and stretched.

Danny saw her eggs. He looked and counted.

In school he drew a picture of the nest with nine pale green eggs in it.

"How lovely," said his teacher. "They'll have ducklings inside, growing."

Danny visited the duck every day. Children played in the playground. Parents passed close by on the footpath. But no one saw.

275

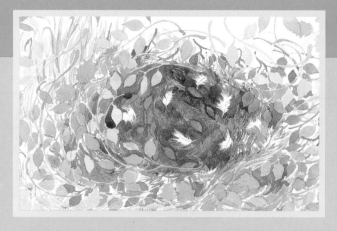

One sunny morning, just as he always did, Danny ran into the playground and over to the pile of brushwood.

But the duck wasn't there. Nor were her eggs. The nest was empty. Danny cried. He cried and cried.

In school he drew a picture of the empty nest. But when his teacher saw the picture – she smiled!

"The mother duck eats the egg-shells," she said, "after the eggs have hatched."

At lunch-time, Danny took his teacher across the playground to the pile of brushwood.

There was the nest.

Then his teacher took Danny
across the school field, to the pond.
Danny looked.
"There's my duck!" he shouted.
"And – one, two, three, four, five,
six, seven, eight, *nine ducklings!*"
And everyone came to see.

Rosie's Babies

by **Martin Waddell**

illustrated by **Penny Dale**

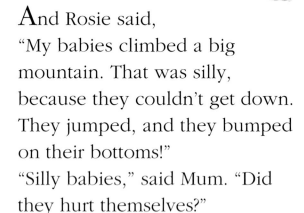

Mum was putting the baby to bed and Rosie said,
"I've got two babies and you've only got one."
"Two, including you," said Mum.
"I'm not a baby, I'm four years old," said Rosie.
"Tell me about your babies," Mum said.

And Rosie said,
"My babies live in a bird's nest and they are nearly as big as me. They go out in the garden all by themselves and sometimes they make me cross!"
"Do they?" said Mum.
"Yes, when they do silly things!" said Rosie.
"What silly things do they do?" asked Mum.

And Rosie said,
"My babies climbed a big mountain. That was silly, because they couldn't get down. They jumped, and they bumped on their bottoms!"
"Silly babies," said Mum. "Did they hurt themselves?"

rockers and dinosaurs. They go to the park when it's dark and there are no mums and dads who can see, only me!"

"Gracious!" said Mum.

"Aren't they scared?"

And Rosie said,
"One of my babies hurt her knee.
I bandaged it up and she cried
and I said 'Never mind' because
I am kind."

"I'm sure you are," said Mum.
"What else do your babies do?"

And Rosie said,
"My babies drive cars that are
real ones and lorries and
dumpers and boats. My babies
are very good drivers."

"What do your babies like
doing best?" asked Mum.

And Rosie said,
"My babies like swings and

And Rosie said,
"My babies are scared of the
big dog, but I'm not.
I know the big dog. I go
'Blackie, sit,' and he does."
"They are not very scared
then?" said Mum.
"My babies know I will
look after them," said Rosie.
"I'm their mum."
"How do you look after
them?" Mum asked.

And Rosie said,
"I make their teas and I tell
them stories and I take them for
walks and I talk to them and I tell
them that I love them."
"That's a good way to look after
babies!" said Mum. "Do you
make them nice things to eat,
like pies?"

And Rosie said,
"My babies make their own
pies, but they never eat them."
"What do they eat?" asked Mum.

And Rosie said,
"My babies eat apples and

And Rosie thought and
thought and thought and
then Rosie said,
"My babies have gone to bed."
"Just like this one," said Mum.
"I don't want to talk about my
babies any more because they
are asleep," said Rosie. "I don't
want them to wake up, or
they'll cry."
"We could talk very softly,"
said Mum.
"Yes," said Rosie.
"What will we talk about?"
asked Mum.

And Rosie said
"ME!"

apples and apples all the
time. And grapes and pears
but they don't like the pips."
"Most babies don't," said
Mum.
"Are you going to tell me
more about your babies?"

Can't You Sleep, Little Bear?

by Martin Waddell • *illustrated by Barbara Firth*

Once there were two bears. Big Bear and Little Bear. Big Bear is the big bear, and Little Bear is the little bear.

They played all day in the bright sunlight. When night came, and the sun went down, Big Bear took Little Bear home to the Bear Cave.

Big Bear put Little Bear to bed in the dark part of the cave.

"Go to sleep, Little Bear," he said.

And Little Bear tried.

Big Bear settled in the Bear Chair and read his Bear Book, by the light of the fire. But Little Bear couldn't get to sleep.

"Can't you sleep, Little Bear?" asked Big Bear, putting down his Bear Book (which was just getting to the interesting part) and padding over to the bed.

"I'm scared," said Little Bear.

"Why are you scared, Little Bear?" asked Big Bear.

"I don't like the dark," said Little Bear.

"What dark?" said Big Bear.

"The dark all around us," said Little Bear.

Big Bear looked, and he saw that the dark part of the cave was very dark, so he went to the Lantern Cupboard and took out the tiniest lantern that was there. Big Bear lit the tiniest lantern, and put it near to Little Bear's bed.

"There's a tiny light to stop you being scared, Little Bear," said Big Bear.

"Thank you, Big Bear," said Little Bear, cuddling up in the glow.

"Now go to sleep, Little Bear," said Big Bear, and he padded back to the Bear Chair and settled down to read the Bear Book, by the light of the fire.

Little Bear tried to go to sleep, but he couldn't.

"Can't you sleep, Little Bear?" yawned Big Bear, putting down his Bear Book (with just four pages to go to the interesting bit) and padding over to the bed.

"I'm scared," said Little Bear.

"Why are you scared, Little Bear?" asked Big Bear.

"I don't like the dark," said Little Bear.

"What dark?" asked Big Bear.

"The dark all around us," said Little Bear.

"But I brought you a lantern!" said Big Bear.

"Only a tiny-weeny one," said Little Bear. "And there's lots of dark!"

Big Bear looked, and he saw that Little Bear was quite right, there was still lots of dark. So Big Bear went to the Lantern Cupboard and took out a bigger lantern. Big Bear lit the lantern, and put it beside the other one.

"Now go to sleep, Little Bear," said Big Bear and he padded back to the Bear Chair and settled down to read the Bear Book, by the light of the fire.

Little Bear tried and tried to go to sleep, but he couldn't.

"Can't you sleep, Little Bear?" grunted Big Bear, putting down his Bear Book (with just three pages to go) and padding over to the bed.

"I'm scared," said Little Bear.

"Why are you scared, Little Bear?" asked Big Bear.

"I don't like the dark," said Little Bear.

"What dark?" asked Big Bear.

"The dark all around us," said Little Bear.

"But I brought you two lanterns!" said Big Bear. "A tiny one and a bigger one!"

"Not much bigger," said Little Bear. "And there's still lots of dark."

Big Bear thought about it, and then he went to the Lantern Cupboard and took out the Biggest Lantern of Them All, with two handles and a bit of chain. He hooked the lantern up above Little Bear's bed.

"I've brought you the Biggest Lantern of Them All!" he told Little Bear. "That's to stop you being scared!"

"Thank you, Big Bear," said Little Bear, curling up in the glow and watching the shadows dance.

"Now go to sleep, Little Bear," said Big Bear and he padded back to the Bear Chair and settled down to read the Bear Book, by the light of the fire.

Little Bear tried and tried and tried to go to sleep, but he couldn't.

"Can't you sleep, Little Bear?" groaned Big Bear, putting down his Bear Book (with just two pages to go) and padding over to the bed.

"I'm scared," said Little Bear.

"Why are you scared, Little Bear?" asked Big Bear.

"I don't like the dark," said Little Bear.

"What dark?" asked Big Bear.

"The dark all around us," said Little Bear.

"But I brought you the Biggest

Lantern of Them All, and there isn't any dark left," said Big Bear.

"Yes, there is!" said Little Bear. "There is, out there!" And he pointed out of the Bear Cave, at the night.

Big Bear saw that Little Bear was right. Big Bear was very puzzled. All the lanterns in the world couldn't light up the dark outside.

Big Bear thought about it for a long time, and then he said, "Come on, Little Bear."

"Where are we going?" asked Little Bear.

"Out!" said Big Bear.

"Out into the darkness?" said Little Bear.

"Yes!" said Big Bear.

"But I'm scared of the dark!" said Little Bear.

"No need to be!" said Big Bear, and he took Little Bear by the paw and led him out from the cave into the night and it was … DARK!

"Ooooh! I'm scared," said Little Bear, cuddling up to Big Bear. Big Bear lifted Little Bear, and cuddled him, and said, "Look at the dark, Little Bear." And Little Bear looked.

"I've brought you the moon, Little Bear," said Big Bear. "The bright yellow moon, and all the twinkly stars."

But Little Bear didn't say anything, for he had gone to sleep, warm and safe in Big Bear's arms.

Big Bear carried Little Bear back into the Bear Cave, fast asleep and he settled down with Little Bear on one arm and the Bear Book on the other, cosy in the Bear Chair by the fire.

And Big Bear read the Bear Book right to …

THE END

Index

Each story and poem in this collection has
been previously published by Walker Books Ltd
87 Vauxhall Walk, London SE11 5HJ

This edition published 2001

2 4 6 8 10 9 7 5 3 1

Printed in Hong Kong

British Library Cataloguing in Publication Data:
a catalogue record for this book
is available from the British Library

ISBN 0-7445-6745-9